KING CHEETAH

LENA GODSALL BOTTRIELL

King Cheetah

THE STORY OF THE QUEST

E.J. BRILL
LEIDEN · NEW YORK· KØBENHAVN · KÖLN
1987

Cover design: Marius Brouwer, Haarlem, The Netherlands

Library of Congress Cataloging-in-Publication Data

Bottriell, Lena Godsall.
  King Cheetah.

  Bibliography: p.
  Includes index.
  1. Cheetahs. I. Title.
QL737.C23B68   1987   599.74'428   87-23891

ISBN 90 04 08588 2

PRINTED IN THE NETHERLANDS BY E. J. BRILL

Contents

Acknowledgments

At the end of a long project, I speak for both Paul and myself in extending heartmost thanks to: OCL for assisting in the transportation; Avon for their super 8 ply tyres and their support; Sabena's U.K. Publicity Officer Noreena Parker for her enthusiastic support; Sue Hartwig and staff of Sabena's South African office for their help and patience; Namib Airways; Toyota South Africa for the continued use of their splendid vehicles; Ms. Daphne Hills of the British Museum of Natural History; Mr. M. J. Austwick of Barclays Bank; John Moger of the Daily Mail.

A special thank you to our friend and colleague Phorego Gulubane whose good humour and willingness were a godsend.

Our gratitude to: the late President of Botswana, Sir Seretse Khama and his Administrative Secretary; the Department of Wildlife, National Parks & Tourism, Botswana, and its Director Mr. E. T. Matenge; Mr. T. R. Ngwako, Assistant Game Warden, Machaneng.

Our gratitude also to: the Zimbabwe Department of National Parks and Wild Life Management; Lieutenant-Colonel Hank Meyer, and Major Richard Stannard for the patient consideration they gave our request; the Bottriell family in Zimbabwe.

And sincere thanks to: Dr. Reay Smithers for access to his research; Sir Archibald James for his interest and help; Mr. Lawrie Davidson for the photograph of the Wild King Cheetah reproduced in this book; Dr. A. M. Brynard, Director of the National Parks Board, and Dr. U. de V. Pienaar for making the Kruger Park search possible; Game Rangers Pat Woolf and Ted Whitfield and their respective Game Scouts and the numerous other Kruger Park personnel who cheerfully came to our aid; Dr. Hilary Keogh of the Institute of Medical Research in Johannesburg for the hair analysis; the Director and Staff of African Oxygen; the former Director of Pretoria Zoo, Dr. D. Brand, and the present Director Dr. Willie Labuschagne, and their staff; Maria Beaconsfield of Witwatersrand University; Professor Malcolm Funston for the use of the termograph; Professor Brian Preston and Dr. Norman Cartright of Wits Dental School for the teeth moulds; Charles Norman of Scope Magazine; Des Varaday of Loskop Cheetah Sanctuary for his hospitality and permission to photograph; Mr. and Mrs. Garne Penny who befriended us and in a hundred ways helped us; Jan Hamman of *Beeld* for his wizardry with the camera and excellent photographs; Willie du Plessis and Canon Cameras; Rex Sevenoaks for his conviviality and assistance; Paul Bosman for the pattern sketches of the Ivy's King Cheetah skins; Roger Miller, Rodney Crouch and Ian Wheatley of Holiday Inns for their hospitality; Mr. Jan Jourbert for his kindness in allowing us the use of the ''Messina'' skin and his continuing friendship; Ossie and Gary Schoof for their film of the Kruger Park King Cheetah; Monty Fuhr of Tuli Lodge; and Geoff Hall for a donation that came from the heart. I'd also like to express our gratitude to Mr. Mendel Levin for his staunch advice.

Naturally there are many others not included to whom I nonetheless express our thanks, as I do to the following:

Agfa-Gevaert Ltd.
Addis Ltd.
Avis South Africa
Barclays Bank, South Africa
Beeld
Bledlow Ridge Primary School
Berec (Everready) Ltd.
Brook Bond Oxo Ltd.
Daily Mail
Decimo Ltd.
Dr. Edward H. Elston
Everite
Gifford Newton & Sons Ltd.
Harcostar
Holiday Inns
Holy Cross Convent, Chalfont
    St. Peter

I.C.I. South Africa
Jasco (Handic Radios) South
    Africa
Jeyes Ltd.
Kgalagadi Breweries, Botswana
Nuffield Laboratories
Paterson Jenks Plc.
Pretoria Mammal Research Unit
Princess Risborough Garage
Rennies Consolidated Holdings
Schweppes Ltd.
Sentrachem
Siemens
Stellenbosch Farmers Wineries
South African Museum Cape
    Town

Square One Computer Services Ltd.
The Ryvita Company Ltd.
The Zoological Society of London
Total South Africa
Trek Petroleum
T.W. Generators
W. Norris Bazzard
Whitworths Holdings Ltd.
World Expeditionary Association

And of course my special thanks to the characters who appear in this book not mentioned here.

Lena Godsall Bottriell

Foreword

At first I was reluctant to write a foreword to this book. When asked to write such a piece it is to get my opinion about a subject from a zoological—and more specifically a cryptozoological—viewpoint. But, in this instance, how could I present my own view without disclosing the true identity of the King Cheetah? It would be rather like lending a detective story to a friend and simultaneously, if inadvertently, blurting out the name of the murderer—a villanous part for me to play, indeed.

But, although the present story is as full of suspense as any Agatha Christie or Ruth Rendell creation, it is not merely a whodunit. This became obvious to me as soon as I started reading it. I knew the ending and most of the episodes of the story, but still I could hardly put it aside even under the pressure of hunger, sleep, or any other earth-bound demands. Why, this book soon had me as artfully spellbound as an adventure novel in the great tradition leading from Rider Haggard to Wilbur Smith! And no wonder, as it tells the story—the true story, mind you—of a long, strenuous, and sometimes nerve-racking quest among the sundry hazards of wildest nature, under the ever-present threat of frightening beasts and representatives of the *Homo sapiens* species, known as guerillas or terrorists—considerably more terrifying fellows than the thugs, hashshashins, and cannibals of yore.

Moreover, as all this took place in Africa, the continent I have been in love with since I wandered through it leisurely from the Cape to the source of the Nile, Lena Bottriell's very lively narrative irresistibly brought back to me memories of many enchanting days, among others at Satara (Kruger Park) where, by a stroke of luck I could have met a King Cheetah! I read the manuscript in a sort of ecstatic trance—but, of course, this was a personal response. Anyway, it seemed to me that I should not spoil the reader's pleasure by merely stressing the scientific importance of the results of the Bottriell quest which was more in the nature of a checking of the evidence than of a completely new discovery. Indeed, I had already applied to the Bottriells for the details of their own achievements which will appear in an as yet unpublished book of mine, *The Still Unknown Cats of Africa* (these are surprisingly numerous), in which an entire chapter is devoted to the King Cheetah. The "scientific" discovery of the King Cheetah dates from 1926—almost sixty years ago. The systematic status of this feline has been controversial ever since. Here, for instance, is the summary of the situation I published, some thirty years ago, in my book *On the Track of Unknown Animals* in which I predicted the true nature of the animal:

> "...it is by no means proved that the king cheetah is a new species. Many zoologists think it may merely be a matter of individuals with abnormal markings. From an evolutionary point of view, the spotted coat of many felines derives from a primitive striped coat; the spots are due to the stripes breaking up. In domestic cats one can sometimes see several intermediate stages between spots and stripes all in the same litter. In the spotted species of felines stripes may reappear as a result of atavism in certain individuals. Thus several very rare cases of striped leopards have been described, and there is no doubt that they belong to the known species.
> "It is therefore not impossible that striped cheetahs may also be rare abnormalities. The fact that the few known specimens all come from the same area does seem to contradict this theory. But there could well be ecological reasons which favoured these abnormal offspring, or these abnormalities could be connected with the genetical ancestry of a group of animals in a confined area."

The Bottriells conducted a painstaking search for skins of specimens (increasing the number known from 11 in 1978 to 22 at present) and for reports of sightings of living specimens, whether or not these were supported by photographs and/or cine films. They established, as accurately as was possible, the geographical boundaries of the aberrant form of the cheetah and also showed that it is generally found in heavily wooded areas, often being active at night and sometimes taking to water—habits which are far from normal for "ordinary" cheetahs.

12

It seems that where the cheetah is pre-eminently a plains runner, diurnal because of its specialised hunting technique of coursing and running down its prey which it must be able to see clearly, individuals royally adorned—thanks to a genetical accident—with stripes and blotches tend to plunge into the forest and to hunt at night, actually by stalking.

It may well be that cheetahs, having been driven off the savannas by the encroachments of agricultural and urban civilisation, are more inclined to dwell near the verges of accessible forests and even to take refuge in them permanently. In such an environment, of course, they would have to change their predatory habits because their unequalled speed would be of limited advantage. Such a change of habitat may be detrimental to the species as a whole but it could favour the few striped examples of it, these being better camouflaged and consequently safer in a forested environment. Natural selection would ensure that striped cheetahs would become more numerous than cheetahs marked conventionally. Because of their conventional unostentatious livery the ordinary cheetahs will either vanish in the woods gradually or drift back into their original surroundings.

Eventually the African cheetah's stock would be split into two very distinct varieties: a savanna form, spotted and diurnal; and a forest form, striped and nocturnal. Living in adjacent but differing habitats the representatives of both forms would have decreasing opportunities to mate. From being mere individual colour phases they would finally become geographical races, or rather subspecies, which might some day evolve into full species.

If the King Cheetah is "just a freak, an occasional mutation", as some have insisted, then its story may seem somewhat disappointing from the restricted cryptozoological viewpoint, since cryptozoology is the systematic search for unknown animal species about which testimonial and/or circumstantial evidence is available. But the situation certainly has a brighter look from the broader zoological viewpoint. Even more exciting than the discovery of a species new to Science is the discovery of a species new to Nature. Evolution is a most mysterious—and thus still controversial—

process, so intricate that no-one has ever been able to reproduce it experimentally, so slow that it seems we may only interpret it by glancing through the palaeontological record. But is it really impossible to watch the mechanisms of evolution, to witness a species in the making? Why, this is precisely what the quest for the King Cheetah could have made possible. Lo and behold, evolution in action!

Even in the realm of cryptozoology proper this book should prove to be invaluable because it is packed with practical advice for would-be expeditionaries, especially for those who dream of dashing off in pursuit of some still undiscovered animal. One of the commonest criticisms levelled at cryptozoologists is that they have never, as yet, caught the hare they were after. This is quite untrue. Long before I coined the word "cryptozoology" in the late fifties several distinguished members of the Animal Kingdom, previously known through fantastic traditions, native legends, travellers' tales, or simple rumours, have been discovered after many years of empirical investigation. I need only single out the mountain tapir of the high Andes, the okapi of the Congo rain-forest, and the giant squid of the ocean depths. It is true that during recent decades some thoughtless enthusiasts, ignoring the principles of cryptozoology but still often calling themselves cryptozoologists, went a-hunting some *rara avis* which, inevitably, revealed itself as a "wild goose". I recall many an Abominable Snowman expedition which looked for the *yeti* at altitudes where no primate could subsist. I recall also a dinosaur hunt in the Cameroons based entirely upon the much embroidered experience of someone who was a brilliant science-writer but who was—alas!—quite incapable of reporting events without distorting them to make a journalistic splash—a remarkable case of mythomania. And, much more recently, there has been a rather futile search for a mermaid-like creature in the South Pacific where the presence of the dugong was the obvious answer. These failures were the result of unpreparedness and lack of useful information: a successful hunt for an unknown animal must be preceded by long, sometimes dull pauses in museums, laboratories, libraries, and newspaper

14

archives. This is one of the lessons to be learnt from the present exemplary quest.

Although I have said I was reluctant to write this foreword I do so because my early prognostication of the King Cheetah's identity has turned out to be more or less correct; and because I think it is my duty to venture another prophecy which comes irrepressibly to my pen. I am sure Lena Bottriell's opus will sooner or later become a classic among printed zoological travelogues, such as some of the best works of two great friends of mine, the late Ivan T. Sanderson and the still active and kicking Gerry Durrell. It so happens that, more than a quarter of a century ago, Gerry wrote an enthusiastic introduction to my own *On the Track of Unknown Animals*. To be fair, I owe a debt to the writer of a good book on a similar subject—and that's that. Incidentally, I am not wondering which cryptozoological narrative Lena Bottriell, in her turn, could be asked to preface herself within the next thirty years—just to carry on this unusual literary relay race. I am afraid there may not be much wildlife left to write about in the twenty-first century. No, what I am looking forward to is the news of another unknown beastie which Lena and her adventurous husband are going to track and hopefully bag in the near future.

Bernard Heuvelmans, D.Sc., F.Z.S.
President, International Society
of Cryptozoology.

Prologue

After what seemed a myriad corridors, floors and winding stairs, we arrived at a pair of heavy, bolted double doors hidden away in an obscure corner of the museum. Within minutes we were standing in a room the size of an olympic swimming pool. Row upon neat row of Victorian-style filing cabinets stretched the length and breadth of it like specimens suspended in a hush of ether. Each cabinet was stacked with narrow drawers suitable for laying out animal skins flat and smoothed over with naphthalene crystals to preserve their quality under storage. Here, among the animal-skin archives of the Natural History Museum at South Kensington, London, in one of the many polished drawers, a King Cheetah pelt had been preserved. It had been here since 1937, about ten years after Lionel Walter, second Baron Rothschild, had acquired it for his private museum at Tring Park, Hertfordshire.

One of the most remarkable collections of zoological specimens ever accumulated by an individual, this private museum was bequeathed in its entirety to the Trustees of the British Museum on the condition that it was kept as an annexe of the Natural History Museum, thereby remaining a centre for research. Baron Rothschild died in 1937 and the skin in question was removed to London where it has been part of the study collection ever since, joining the museum's only mounted King Cheetah specimen. Purchased in 1928 from Rowland Ward's, the renowned game measurers and taxidermists, it had previously been on public display. But because of a deterioration in its condition, it too now reposed in the skin archives, out of sight. Here, with no information other than its name, in the northern hemisphere during the glorious jubilee summer of 1977, was the sum total of all that was known about the King Cheetah, the Cheetah with stripes down its back. There were literary references around but they amounted to little more than a discrete line or two. With its proverbial one-eyed

King Cheetah pelt on left. Common cheetah, right. Both from British Natural History Museum, London. Note the King Cheetah's three dorsal stripes, and irregular blotches all over flanks.

vision—Blake's famous challenge, for which there is much to be said—science is blind to inconvenient evidence and the King Cheetah was a perfect case in point. Nothing scientific, nothing controversial, nothing new about the animal had emerged since the 1930s. For the enquiring mind with a spirit to match this was a spur to action.

Over a cheeky bohemian lunch and the sweet, warm, hedonistic feel of great and impossible things to come which good wine and atmosphere has the delicious knack of conjuring up, what had previously seemed just a boyish whim of Paul's, the delightfully individual colonial I had married, was beginning to acquire a raffish tone of seriousness. By the time he had said, "Come, let me show you Africa...", I needed little persuading. My addled romantic's mind was already awash with thoughts of bushing it in the Africa of my Kipling and Rider Haggard days; a last, great safari. The seed was sown, simply, spontaneously. In a bid to solve the riddle of this striped pimpernel among cats, the King Cheetah that had captured the imagination of but a few before us, we would

In the heat of the day, but still ever watchfull, a cheetah lies up in wooded cover.

mount an expedition to southern Africa—the "last great safari", as it would indeed come to be known.

As with any such undertaking, objectives had to be defined from the start. Unlike the lion, tiger or leopard which are all of the genus *Panthera* though separate species, the modern cheetah is the sole living member of the genus *Acinonyx*. It is the most specialised of the big cats. It is also one of the most monomorphic species yet discovered; that is to say, there is little genetic variation to speak of within the species. The cheetah has shown remarkable uniformity in both type and markings throughout its formerly wide distribution in much of India, in Africa from the Cape to Cairo and all suitable regions between to south-west Asia. Consequently, notable pattern variations are so rare in cheetahs that they are virtually non-existent. By contrast, there are eight accepted subspecies of tiger; while in leopards, in which single-pattern aberrations are common enough, some thirty have been named and described! Comparison with the cheetah couldn't be greater; small wonder that the emergence of the King Cheetah should pose such an enticing puzzle. Indeed, it is without doubt the most unexpected, uniquely patterned big cat to be chronicled in modern times.

A uniformity of pattern has been observed in nearly forty recorded specimens. This comprises bold black-brown markings embossed, or raised above, a cream base—the result of the black hairs being at greater angles to the skin than those of the background—on a coat characterised by softer, silkier, longer hair, broad dorsal stripes, irregular blotches and a striped and ringed tail found in no other big cat. This combination of features remains unchanged in all King Cheetah specimens available for examination (beyond the acceptable degree of deviation between members of the same-patterned mammal species). The regular appearance of such a pattern on a large animal this century in southern Africa is the more remarkable for being associated with such a species. There exist no intermediate coat patterns between the King Cheetah and the common cheetah. There is no record of a freak cheetah pattern remotely like it. No felid species in Africa or Asia has been documented as producing, at intervals, a consistently uniform and similarly distinctive pattern variation displaying such a marked divergence from the norm—and being consistent in its occurrence over a wide yet restricted geographic area. Thus, apart from proving its existence, our most ambitious goal would be to endeavour to ascertain the King Cheetah's position on the genetic tree. A recessive form? A throwback to the original cheetah perhaps? A species in its own right? A sub-species or race? The offspring of a hybrid cross somewhere back in past millenia? A local mutation; a simple aberration?

Significantly enough, the King Cheetah had already been accorded species status, as *Acinonyx rex*, in 1927 by Reginald Pocock, curator of mammals at the Natural History Museum in London and an authority on the felines. Two years later, the King Cheetah was given full generic status in Hungary, as the only species of the completely new genus *Paracinonyx*, by the controversial taxonomist Miklos Kretzoi. In 1939 Pocock retracted his classification on the grounds of insufficient evidence. Kretzoi did not retract his. Therefore, in aiming to increase the current field knowledge of the King Cheetah and in effect to re-open the question of the animal's status, our immediate objectives were clear, with each dictating its own course. These were: to evaluate and collate previously unrecorded skins and sightings; to trace and verify any new sightings and skins, obtaining photographs of the latter; trace a skull and either all, or part, of a skeleton for analysis purposes; to locate and photograph a live King Cheetah, capturing it if possible, and to extract small samples of blood and tissue from it for genetic analysis; and finally, perhaps, to encourage the authorities of an appropriate wildlife body, preferably established in the African sub-continent, to institute a breeding programme so as to isolate the strain.

A skull alone of a King Cheetah would be of particular significance, given the possibility of its proving to be different to that of the common cheetah. As for locating live King Cheetahs, let alone obtaining photographs or films of it, we generously estimated our chances as being 99.9% against! In essence we were

British Museum flat King Cheetah skin, bequeathed from the Rothschild Collection.

embarking on a quest to solve the riddle of an enigma—"a needle in a haystack" as the BBC put it to us in a television interview—the discovery of a creature that, according to some pundits, could not be classified as real or imaginary. Its continued existence was strongly refuted in some scientific quarters; in others, silly as it may seem, its past existence was doubted also, even against the evidence of King Cheetah pelts. "One-eyed vision" indeed. Hence our first priority: to see if the King Cheetah could still be found in southern Africa, its considered domain, fifty years on.

Before any fieldwork could get under way, there were the obvious preliminaries of raising finance and sponsorship, organising equipment, obtaining the sanction of relevant governments, obtaining the necessary permits etc. Another was publicity, as much a concomitant of our continuing research as the planned search itself, given the fragmented nature of the exercise and the relative obscurity of the King Cheetah. On arrival at our destination it would be essential, therefore, that we launch a publicity campaign through the press and other media aimed specifically at obtaining information on the King Cheetah, particularly records of recent sightings. A private project such as ours would have an advantage over similar expeditions undertaken by official delegations from zoos, museums, universities and the like, because we would not have to fall in with any established dogmas and criteria. It would leave us free to talk to game officials, hunters, dealers, poachers and villagers alike without the bogey of misinterpretations of our views being reflected on some auspicious body. Even with urban-dwellers in the bigger towns, some of whom have never been in the bush in their lives even though they live in Africa, it is amazing how much "evidence" they may have tucked away in attics, family albums, or just in the weathered storehouse of memory... some treasured tales of grandfather's forays with a gun.

Fieldwork would be of prime importance and would initially involve a systematic ground search of a specific area. We had three choices of geographical areas, based on an overview of where King Cheetahs had been shot or sighted since the animal had been first brought to public attention in 1926: the north-eastern corner of the

Tuli Block in Botswana in and around the confluence of the Shashe and Limpopo rivers; the lush eastern strip of Zimbabwe bordering Mozambique; and central Kruger Park edging northeast toward Mozambique. At that time Rhodesia (as it then was) boasted the greatest number of skins and sightings recorded to date, but the impending war situation made that country an impractical choice. Tuli offered a different scenario. A remote zone of roughly 700 sq.kms nestling snugly in the confluence area of the Shashe and Limpopo between Zimbabwe and South Africa, it was here, just south of the Tuli Circle, that the latest reputed sighting of a King Cheetah had occurred; this had been confirmed by reliable sources in southern Africa via the Natural History Museum in London. Thus Tuli became our first area of operation, although we did not arrogantly assume it would supply the answer. Zimbabwe (as it was to become) and Kruger were both to play a vibrant part eventually.

Legend

"Ati, Bwana! There is a story you will not believe, because you are a white man. White men laugh at the stories told by the black men. They say this is not so, and that is not so. We have not seen this or that, so how can it be? They say, Ho, Ho! Black men are like little children, telling tales to each other in the dark. But remember, *bwana*, white men have been in this country for a time that is less than the life of one man, so how can you know all the things that have been known to black men for a hundred lifetimes and more?"

Ali, to Roger Courtney: *'Greenhorn In Africa'*

Childhood's dreams are often left at the foot of the bed with the other shed hopes and romantic schemes, faded blobs of cow gum in scrapbooks their only remaining memory. For some the fantasies don't fade with the flush of youth; time and determination shape them into existence instead. It couldn't be otherwise—those brought up in a land where little gets left to the past, time being all present, already live in the hereafter of their dreams, life being the dream. Thus little gets left to memory. It's only the harsh realities of day-to-day existence that cause man's lofty spires to become dim in the distance. In the mists of human exigency those spires are, needless to say, the fuel of life. Thank heavens, then, for the Lewis Carrolls of this world who nurture in youthful minds an early faith in mystic isles; mystic isles abounding in wonders of any choosing: shells like miracles that speak of the sea; winged flowers in butterflies and moths; swallows... nature's tiny flying machines; magic-evoking animals, from noble striped stallions to heraldic unicorns—creatures and creations of every description as well as those that defy depiction. There was one we knew of, a silken cat, that had often challenged the regal might of the tiger and the lion, yet was no mere mythical inhabitant of any mystic isle. It was the King Cheetah, named for the regal splendour of its appearance. Yet, long before officialdom found it, legend knew it as the *nsuifisi*.

For many years, during the early days of colonisation in south-east Africa, Africans had told white hunters of an animal that was neither lion, leopard nor cheetah. The notorious "hyena-leopard", or nsuifisi, had had many peculiar tales woven about it, believed as it was by the Africans of Manicaland to be a cross between a leopard and a hyena. It raided kraals at night, often devastating the pens where stock was kept as it slaughtered indiscriminately, before making off with a sheep or a goat. Though lithe and with semi-retractile claws, it was said to look like a leopard. But instead of spots it was boldly barred in black and white, like the striped hyena. Many in authority ridiculed the stories as just the superstitious myths of Africans, comparable to other tales of prowling cats such as the brindled nunda, known for over six centuries to the Africans of the East African coast; the mysterious ntarago of Kenya; or the Uganda forest's savage, howling ndalawo. But according to Captain William Hichens, the nsuifisi, far from being a myth, was an entirely new species of cheetah, known as the King Cheetah. An officer with the Intelligence and Administrative Services of East Africa and a keen sportsman, Hichens had often written of the nsuifisi; perceptively had reasoned that a leopard-hyena cross is exactly how the nsuifisi, or King Cheetah, would look to anyone other than a skilled zoologist. Others remarked how extraordinary it was that such a remarkable animal could exist, yet for so long be unknown to science. But similar cries had been echoed before with the Okapi and the Congo peacock, for it is a sentiment familiar to many who have been involved in the discovery or pursuit of a "hidden", legendary animal.

Walking on African soil was for me an unknown quantity and in the light of the particular war-torn chunk of sub-continent to which Paul and I would soon be heading, such a prospect offered an awesome challenge to someone with only a literary understanding of Africa. Yet one can so easily exaggerate the perils, forgetting in the process the character of one's own country. Being no stranger to the drowsy throb of the bush at noontide, having been born and brought up in Australia in the wake of pioneer stock, I have fortunately inherited an innate veneration for the sweep of a bronze-shouldered plain, the grandeur of lush green sanctuaries under endless, forever blue skies. That simple mathematical combination of stark wild beauty and nature's hidden unpredictabilities leaves me breathless. I hoped that Africa would impress me in the same way.

Paul needed no such reassurances. While still a small boy in Africa, intimations of the existence of a mysterious striped cheetah had made an abiding impression. He'd learned to hunt by the time he'd turned ten, shooting mainly for the pot, the art of discrimation having already made itself felt even at that young age. Thus it was only a matter of time before a natural desire to preserve what he could so easily neutralise with the soft thud of a bullet should take hold of him; that is why taxidermy became a hobby of his. Contrary to what some might argue it is often the thinking hunter who makes the best possible conservationist. Understanding the mechanisms of nature, ones reverence for it is at one and the same time emotive and balanced, without the cloying sentimentality that destroys more than it builds. Thus we shared an invaluable attribute in an appreciation of the wild and as such held no contrived feelings towards the adventure ahead.

It was to the Queen Victoria Museum overlooking Salisbury Park in the Rhodesia of the 50s that Paul gravitated so as to learn something of the finer points of taxidermy; there, too, he heard about an enigmatic big cat known as the King Cheetah. It was the avuncular old gentleman in charge of the museum's stuffed exhibits—Paul's "Uncle Remus"—who first fired his imagination with magic-sounding tales of "the handsomest member of the cat tribe" as the King Cheetah was once described by Pocock.

Old Mr. Powell had been among the early pioneers to this part of Africa and enchanted Paul with colourful stories of the Zulu and King Chaka, Lo Benguala and the Matabele Rebellion, David Livingstone, the ill-fated Shangani Patrol and the sterling adventures of Frederick Courteney Selous one of the most famed of Africa's so-called "great white hunters". Such tales of an Africa as yet unfettered sounded chords of delight in the little boy's ears—it was all there, the freedom and scope of a wondrous continent set upon a stage brimming with an infinite variety of wild life. Imagine, if you will, if you've ever loved an animal—indeed if you are one to thrill to the pulsing panorama of nature—witnessing from a high hilltop a vast plain, stretching as far as the eye can see, swimming with game not just in its hundreds or thousands, but tens of thousands: a multitude of elephants, buffaloes and zebras, wildebeest and impalas, kudus, elands... and more. That was Africa less than a century ago. The numbers may have dwindled somewhat but there are parts where they are sufficient to conjure up the magic.

Mr Powell's vivid descriptions of the King Cheetah were equally beguiling. "It was neither leopard nor cheetah", Paul was told, uncannily echoing mysterious tales the little boy had heard of savage brindled cats from Tanzania, Kenya and Uganda that were said to be neither lions nor leopards; or, closer to home, the equally ferocious beast the African in his native Rhodesia knew as the "hyena-leopard". It seemed there was much confusion as to whether the King Cheetah still existed or not; it was also referred to as the *Rhodesian cheetah*, the *Mazoe leopard* too, after a place in the north of the country where, according to reliable sources, it was "well-known to natives" in the early part of the century. It was the size of a leopard or a large cheetah, so Paul was told, its spine horizontally etched in broad black stripes converging on the rump before continuing along the tail for about half its length, thence turning into thick rings on the remainder. Describing the rest of the body as being embossed with heavy, black irregular blotches that most resembled large ink-blots, Mr. Powell's lovingly illustrated vignette of the King Cheetah conjured up in the mind's eye of a small boy pictures of an incomparable animal; and, on seeing a rather antiquated drawing that did little justice to its true beauty, he resolved that the world at large would one day come to know more of this unique King Cheetah. Unknown to Paul only some twelve months before in early 1951, the first King Cheetah skin ever to be recorded, the holotype of *Acinonyx rex*—often rumly referred to as "Major Cooper's skin"—had been destroyed.

28

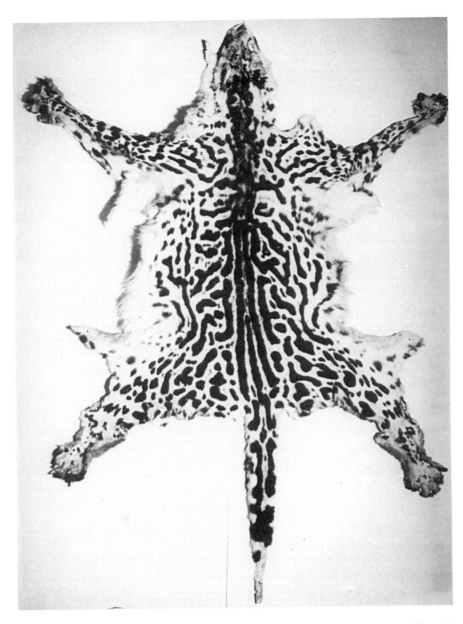

Holotype King Cheetah skin, Queen Victoria Memorial Library and Museum. Collected 1926.

Presented in 1926 to the Queen Victoria Memorial Library and Museum at Salisbury by a farmer from the east of the country, the very uniqueness of the skin subsequently attracted the undivided attention of the curator, a leading naturalist of the day, Major A. L. Cooper. He was immediately reminded of the okapi, that distinctive and secretive antelope with broadly striped legs from the forests of the Congo basin which had been first hinted at by Stanley in 1860 and was later discovered at the turn of the century by Sir Harry Johnson—venerable champion and saviour of the pygmies—who through the fortuitous aid of his tiny protégés firmly established the existence of this queer, mule-like relative of the giraffe. Now strictly protected, it would doubtless be extinct, but for Johnson, given that for some fifty years before its discovery and consequent classification as a new mammal, its meat had been enjoyed at the tables of Belgian officials without much apparent concern about what kind of animal it may or may not have been obtained from.

Cooper wondered if this equally unique cat had been the victim of a similarly blasé attitude and for how long; indeed, he found it difficult to accept how any animal, bearing the extraordinary markings of the skin now in his charge, should and could remain unnoted and he set out to air his views in a paper read on 30th June, 1927 and later published in the South African Journal of Science. It began, somewhat prophetically as it turns out in the light of present-day evidence pointing to the existence of a so-called "sauropod dinosaur" in the northern swamps of the Congo Republic:—

"That this animal was known of for some time past is borne out by the fact that, twenty years ago, mention used to be made round camp fires by natives of a beast that was neither lion, leopard nor cheetah, and, though considered by a number of people to be as mythical as the huge horned water serpent that is supposed to exist in some equatorial swamp, I believe was referred to as the "Mazoe leopard." It was apparently commoner in those days than it is now..."

Disclosures of a further four pelts (obtained through Africans) all sharing that same remarkable degree of parity in pattern (remembering of course that like human fingerprints no two patterned animal skins can ever be exactly identical) can be directly attributed to the Major's enthusiasm, with much of the available information on the striped cheetah being officially recorded for the first time by him. "With the kind permission of the other members of the Queen Victoria Memorial Museum", as he himself so quaintly put it, Cooper arranged for the holotype skin to be sent to the Natural History Museum in London for examination by Prof. Pocock, a distinguished systematist, with whom Cooper had been corresponding on the matter at some length. Pocock had already opined that it might belong to an aberrant, or abnormal, leopard. This was a notion with which Cooper found himself at variance. Admittedly (that is, at least as far as one could judge from the skin) the build of the animal appeared less like the slim, svelte form of the cheetah, and more like the solid, more stocky leopard. This opinion is reflected in the Natural History Museum's mounted King Cheetah specimen, a pelt purchased in 1928, which impresses one at first glance as having been modelled on the lines of a leopard rather than a cheetah. But no undue significance should be attached to this: taxidermists are as much artists as any sculptor and thus are equally open to the trends, influences and opinions of the day.

There was, however, one notable distinction setting it apart from the leopard: the unmistakable non-retractile or partially non-retractile claws of the cheetah, due to an absence of sheaths resulting in the blunt claws remaining always exposed and extended.

Writing in the *Journal of the Society for the Preservation of the Fauna of the Empire* in 1927, Pocock finally gave his considered conclusions:

"A glance at it showed me that it possesses all the characters of the common cheetah, except the pattern, which consists of bold black stripes running longitudinally down the back on to the tail and of shorter more transverse stripes, intermixed with blotches and often looped upon the flanks. Major Cooper also made enquiries in Salisbury to ascertain if any other specimens were known. The result was the discovery that the animal is well known to the natives who fearlessly hunt it with assegaies and that it has been described as the

Mazoe leopard. He was also able to trace four skins in addition to the one that he sent to England, making a total of five taken at different times and in different places, namely in the Umvukwe Range (*sic*), in the Siki Reserve, at Bikita and at Melsetter. With all this evidence available, I did not hesitate to regard the original skin as representing a new species of cheetah which I described...as *Acinonyx rex* in allusion to the splendour of its apparel. But to Major Cooper belongs the credit for the discovery of this magnificent animal which may, I think, without exaggeration, be described as the handsomest member of the cat tribe.''

Perhaps Pocock named it as much for its singularity as for its undeniable beauty, for without doubt it is a king amongst its kin. However, his classification was not well received because of a lack of sound scientific evidence. As early as 1932 Angel Cabrera had suggested that it was no more than an aberrant form of cheetah, while two years later Captain Guy Shortridge talked of it as being a localised mutation coming "only from Southern Rhodesia." There remained Miklos Kretzoi's classic piece of taxonomic one-upmanship in placing *Acinonyx rex*, Pocock's taxon, in the completely new genus, *Paracinonyx*. This suggested that it was not a throwback but was more likely a new type of cheetah in the process of developing, a classification and assessment western science appeared blissfully ignorant of. In 1939 Pocock formally revoked his judgement, upon which investigations into the status of the King Cheetah all but ceased.

Today scientific methods of genetic analysis have advanced to such a level that it is now possible to prove or disprove the taxonomic status of an animal; often a small sample of blood may be all that is required. In the case of the King Cheetah it may be assessed through chromosomal and biochemical genetic testing, as well as skin biopsy, on small samples of blood and tissue taken harmlessly from a living body, with comparisons subsequently drawn between the King and the common cheetah.

Further official comment in scientific circles on the King Cheetah did appear from time to time in later years, but it was of slight importance, largely repeating early research on the subject. There were many discrepancies too, with single skins being treated as

Reginald Innes Pocock (1863-1947). In 1927 he described and classified the King Cheetah as a new species, *Acinonyx rex*. He named it in deference to the regal splendour of its appearance.

two, or museums being attributed with King Cheetah specimens they'd never had, and so on. All the same, in the preliminary stages of organising the expedition, Paul and I did find some old and overlooked references from the last century which were to have some surprising repercussions.

Back in 1952, however, the twelve year old Paul had no knowledge of all this. What he did have was an ineffable sense of quest, and it wasn't long before he was off roaming the hills and kopjes of Mazoe in the Iron Mask Mountains where, some fifty years before, King Cheetahs had wandered. Now, however, only whispered notions about the King Cheetah invaded an atmosphere otherwise brimming with reflections of the past. After traipsing hot and weary around foothills and rocky crests, some days would find Paul ensconced with his faithful ·22 in a shady nook at the top of a kopje overlooking a verdant valley where peaceful farm pastures and citrus orchards now mostly greet the eye. Entranced as much perhaps with the mating antics of a dapper Bateleur eagle—that acrobat of the sky—tumbling and free-falling through the air, as with the inquisitive stares of a cheeky bush squirrel scurrying in and out among the rocks, any young adventurer sitting there amongst those historic, wind-swept terraces might well indeed find himself thinking about gold rush and siege, painted Bushman caves and the early Portuguese, ''Monomotapa'', that supposed, magic-sounding kingdom, or a tiny garrison of pioneers embattled against a thousand 'Shona warriors.

Vibrations of the past are never far away when the very rock speaks of it; why not then memories of a time when it marked the realm of the King Cheetah? But the intervening years of study and growing responsibilities left Paul with less and less time to wonder about such things. He left Africa in 1965 for England, thence for Australia where he found me instead of Cooper's cheetah. That elusive feline, however, was never forgotten; it was merely marking time till its moment of recall.

34

Kings in Grass Castles

"...the publicity now given to the existence of so handsome an animal will surely be taken advantage of by sportsmen and traders. All the big museums in the world will be eager for its skin, and every zoological garden will want live specimens for exhibition. It will, therefore, command a high price, whether alive or dead, and the result will be persecution by hunters and trappers on such a scale as to threaten its extinction..."

Pocock: 1927

It seemed to us vaguely ironic that the choice of the Tuli region in Botswana should fit our plans so fortuitously, given the insidious guerilla war that was being waged just north across the placid reaches of the Shashe.

Bookended as it was at the time by two modern, white-ruled states, the 712,000 square kilometres of the former Bechuanaland Protectorate which had achieved independence from Britain in 1966, is to a large extent unsullied by the so-called western way of life. Consequently, with a population of some 700,000 spread across a vast expanse of land bigger than France, Belgium and the Netherlands put together, Botswana offered us an idyllic scenario for the enactment of the search for history's most obscure cat.

Latest reports indicated that two King Cheetah skins had turned up in eastern Botswana south of the Tuli corner at some time in the mid 1970s. Their whereabouts and origins couldn't be traced although it was believed they may have been auctioned in South Africa. Further to this there was news of actual sightings occurring in Tuli as recently as 1977 just south of an area in Zimbabwe referred to as the Tuli Circle. There was mention too of one or more King Cheetah pelts in the possession of a store-keeper at a place called Lobatse in the southernmost part of the country. A respected authority on the mammals of southern Africa, Dr. Reay Smithers, reported coming across a King Cheetah skin in 1971— subsequently donated by the collector to the National Museum in Gaborone—at Moijabana, a township some 150 kms west of the

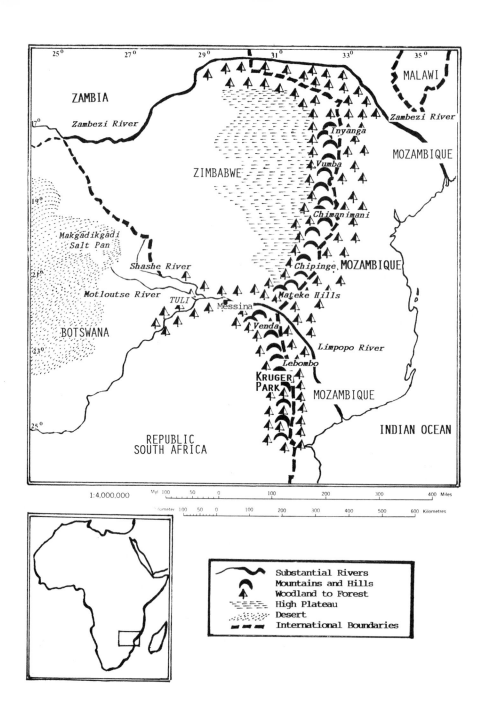

Tuli Block. He dealt with this in his book *Mammals of Botswana*, and again in a paper written some years later in 1980, in both of which he also refers to a report, received on good authority, of sightings of two individuals on a farm in the southern Tuli Block. The existence of more skins, at first only rumoured, was later substantiated, explaining a significant degree of the conjecture surrounding other reports which, ultimately, had not been confirmed.

Certainly, the King Cheetah position in Rhodesia at the time regarding skins and sightings showed striking contrasts; the last skin collected there had been as long ago as 1942, while a single visual record from 1970 marked a lapse of forty years. Thus, all things considered, the data on Botswana, though by appearances "sketchy", added up to one thing, as an official at the Natural History Museum in London gamely observed: "it does seem that Botswana is the best area to aim for".

Having chosen the venue for our field search, it was important that we next obtain from the Botswana government the appropriate permission for the expedition to enter its country. Not unexpectedly, we were powerless to avoid the customary web of red tape that accompanies anything out of the ordinary, especially when it's to do with Africa! Hence, it wasn't till some five months after we had set the bureaucratic wheels in motion that the necessary permission came through, signed and sealed, direct from the office of the President, Gaborone. Meanwhile, fate, that capricious flirt, had shown a hand. Word of a King Cheetah sighting in Kruger Park, South Africa's premier game reserve, had been received at the Natural History Museum in London from Dr. Reay Smithers. This was no ordinary tale: the animal sighted, purportedly within the previous year, *had been photographed!*

Certainly there could have been no more reliable source than Smithers. Beyond actual news of the incident though, he could offer little information on the circumstances surrounding it. Thus it was left to us to get in touch direct with the Kruger Park authorities. As it was the first sighting of a King Cheetah known to be backed by sound photographic evidence a possible search of the reserve could not, in any reasonable estimation, be ruled out.

Reports of King Cheetahs inhabiting Kruger Park had never been officially recorded before and ironically, despite written references to the contrary from the late 1950s to early 1960s, such a possibility had always been treated derisively given the Park's distance from the King's considered domain. Thus, a King Cheetah accidentally photographed by a tourist well towards the south-east of the Park posed an intriguing question: was it not true that, for as long as we could remember, the King Cheetah had been widely regarded as a Rhodesian animal only and that the cats that had turned up in Botswana, for example, had been merely wanderers, compelled to move as a result of the increasing shifts of people across the continent? Few animals respect boundaries, however, and Kruger National Park is vast, covering an area in the north-eastern corner of the Transvaal of approximately 21,000 square kilometres between the Limpopo and Crocodile Rivers, and bounded by the Lebombo Mountain Range along its eastern border with Mozambique. In the light of this, it seems highly unlikely that an animal as distinctively marked as a King Cheetah could enter the topmost end of Kruger Park through the Gonarezhou Reserve (which some in the past believed to be the real home of the King Cheetah) from Zimbabwe, move all the way down the reserve to the South Central District (a distance of 300 kms) where it was photographed; and in all that distance and the period of time it would take to cover such a distance, could go unnoticed and unreported. This would seem to suggest that the King Cheetah photographed so far south was no chance visitor, possibly crossing into the park from Mozambique at a time when no boundary had yet been constructed.

Indeed references discovered in our preliminary research dating back to 1877 suggested that at one time or another cats that sounded suspiciously like forerunners, or at least immature examples, of King Cheetahs (if the early first descriptions are anything to go by), inhabited the Lebombo Mountains dividing Kruger Park from Mozambique. Records of these so-called "woolly cheetahs" have since both gained and lost a great deal in the retelling. In Philip Lutley Sclater's first report on a live specimen newly arrived at the Zoological Society's Gardens in London (1877), he gives it temporary species status as *Felis lanea*, describing it thus:

> "It is male, probably not fully grown. It presents generally the appearance of a Cheetah, but is thicker in the body, and has shorter and stouter limbs, and a much thicker tail. When adult it will probably be considerably larger than the Cheetah, and is larger even now than our three specimens of that animal. The fur is much more woolly and dense than in the Cheetah, as is particularly noticeable on the ears, mane and tail. The whole of the body is of a pale isabelline colour, but covered all over with roundish dark blotches. There are no traces of the black spots which are so conspicuous in all the varieties of the Cheetah which I have seen, nor of the characteristic black line between the mouth and eye".

Later, in 1881, St George Jackson Mivart in *The Cat* adds a stripe to just one side of its muzzle. Still later Richard Lydekker reaffirms that it has blotches in place of normal spots and twice alters its scientific name. Then in the *Royal Natural History* (1893-94) he makes this observation:

> "The Hon. W. H. Drummond states, on the authority of the natives, that in South-East Africa it is very rare, although found more commonly than elsewhere in the rocky gorges of the Bombo (*sic*) Mountains, where it lies concealed in the dense jungle, from which it occasionally ventures forth."

The "Bombo Mountains" to which he refers are, of course, the Lebombos flanking present day Kruger Park. The authorities in the Park were not, however, receptive at this stage to suggestions of our undertaking a search there; the basis for their reasoning was that in their opinion the King Cheetah sighted and photographed represented a freak incident that had not repeated itself since. As such it did not, in the period of time that had elapsed, warrant any follow-up, at least as far as they were concerned.

Although there were cheetahs in the Zoological Society's collection from South Africa, East Africa, Syria and India, Philip Sclater, distinguished Secretary of the Society for many years, wrote that he found it impossible to associate the "woolly cheetah" with any of them. Despite this, the "woolly cheetah" finally comes down to us in contradiction of the earlier descriptions by Sclater and others as the "red-spotted" cheetah, a suggested case of partial albinism which had increased to several specimens with clear differences between them. Of all the big cats it is the cheetah—its biology, ecology and behaviour—that has taken science the longest to get to know. Indeed, it has taken until this century; and we are still learning much about this enigmatic cat, the "spotted sphinx" as Joy Adamson dubbed it. When viewed with the advantage of hindsight, it's little wonder that an even more mysterious and elusive type of cheetah should be so neglected. "Inconvenient evidence" indeed!

Other references we discovered were scant and added little to what was already common knowledge. Nonetheless any information on the King Cheetah passed to us by museums and related bodies in southern Africa, however repetitive, was conveyed as warmly and as helpfully as that we'd received from similar institutions in England. In short, people were receptive to our enquiries. This was especially true of Sir Archibald James. A keen sportsman and former diplomat, he had been inspired, by a chance incident during a shooting trip in Southern Rhodesia in 1960, to undertake research of his own on the King Cheetah, culminating in a review in *The Field*. His sheer enthusiasm for our project was profoundly encouraging; he even wanted to accompany us on the expedition and I don't doubt for a moment that he would have if ill-health had not sorely debilitated him.

With Kruger Park now out of the reckoning, we concluded, when roughly outlining the blueprint for our search in Botswana, that ideally it should incorporate both aerial and ground operations working simultaneously, or at different intervals depending on circumstances of weather, terrain etc. As we'd be working in near virgin bush 4WD vehicles were an obvious necessity. We settled eventually for two second-hand long-wheel-base Landrovers which we duly christened "Ingwe" and "Lulu" from the Zulu for cheetah, *Ingwelulu*. When both vehicles had been sprayed the traditional "sand" colour and the legend" King Cheetah Expedition" had been emblazoned across their flanks, the whole elusive concept

40

Sponsorship is vital! So is getting good photographs, and the roof of the Landrover was a perfect platform.

of searching for the King Cheetah began to take on a tangible sense of reality.

Would that a solution to the problem of aerial transport could be found with the same easy rationale! A fundamental consideration in our choice of craft was, of course, the cost. There were various options open to us: light, fixed-wing aircraft; helicopters; autogyros (motorised hang gliders, or microlites, were not yet operational). Subsequently, we embarked on a fact-finding spate

41

of test flights on flying machines of all types and shapes. The results were varied. Although economically viable, autogyros were impractical. Not only were they too noisy, they did not operate well in areas of extreme temperature fluctuation. On the other hand, fixed-wing craft lacked the flexibility we required in speed and height.

Like motorised hang gliders those other "dream machines", airships—or "blimps" as they are otherwise affectionately known—seemed absolutely ideal. Unfortunately, where we were heading they were about as hard to come by as snow in the Sahara. Expense alone put them out of our reach. Indeed, whatever our choice of aerial transport, it was destined to depend largely on sponsorship. We had an encouraging letter from a firm in southern Africa which marketed helicopters. This was better than nothing, but it didn't take us long to discover a hard truth. Although a great many potential sponsors in the hard world of commerce responded well to our requests for aid, whether in the form of cash donations or goods, there were as many if not more for whom a "romantic quest" such as ours, even though the splendour of it may well have gone some way towards exciting their imaginations, was nonetheless rather too uncomfortably quixotic. Our destination, a wild backwater just north of which a virulent terrorist war was raging, didn't help any!

On specially printed, headed stationery incorporating a handsome logo—an artists's-impression-portrait of a snarling "King"—we sent out floods of requests for sponsorship to commercial organisations as well as to those bodies which award grants to projects of a scientific slant such as ours. The response in the way of free offers of goods, even finance, was gratifying (as was the decision to raise fuel sponsorship and basic domestic needs in Africa). Certainly it was not without variety and included for openers a brand-new, portable, lightweight, electric generator, a collapsible caravan, a portable X-ray unit, a heavy-duty Fairey winch, binoculars, compasses and survey tapes, plus sundry other items, from tyres, camp-beds and tarpaulins to plastic storage containers to hold food enough for a garrison as well as crates of dried fruit, tea and cof-

42

fee... even a cash donation raised by children at the local primary school (which must surely vie for originality with the £100 donation from a small, local computer firm!).

We began negotiating with newspapers and airlines for assistance almost from the day we decided to mount the expedition and fortunately raised sufficient sponsorship from both the "fourth estate" and a major international airline operating direct flights to Johannesburg, the nearest jumping-off point for Botswana, it having no through airlink with Europe.

To help establish the taxonomic status of the King Cheetah in the event of obtaining blood and tissue samples, we solicited the services of the Nuffield Laboratories in London. (Later, the Director of the Mammal Research Unit at the University of Pretoria confirmed that they too would be willing to undertake chromosome and genetic tests thereby acting as an essential cross-reference.) As for getting any specimens of blood and tissue earmarked for analysis from the bush all the way to the Nuffield in Regents Park, it was imperative they reach their destination within 48 hours of collection otherwise a rapid deterioration of the cell structure would threaten the validity of the tests. Obviously, getting the samples through to the Mammal Research unit in Pretoria within the prescribed period wasn't beset with the same degree of urgency. Five 10 ml blood samples for biochemical genetics were to be transported in ice, but not frozen, while a skin biopsy and one 5 ml blood sample for chromosome typing could travel at room temperature. With a local charter firm agreeing to handle the first leg from the bush to Jo'burg, our big flight sponsor, Sabena, undertook to get all the required samples from there to the laboratories at Regents Park without delay. As the Mammal Research Institute was not set up that time to do as complete an analysis as Nuffield, they required only a small amount of blood plasma and washed red blood cells for electrophoretics (examination of molecular function and protein), and a skin biopsy for chromosome preparations from skin cultures.

As regards crew, our solicitors advised us to take out signed, written contracts with whoever we took on as team members. Though a measure that at first seemed a little over the top, there was never better advice given; nor could one give better advice to any would-be organiser of a private expedition. In choosing team members we set but one parameter: they should be young, the basis for our argument being that the opportunities afforded one when young can, in the long run, often benefit a world of others. It was a somewhat altruistic first principle of choice that did in fact eliminate a number of good people!

Be that as it may, we were to take up an offer we couldn't refuse from the chief vet of one of Britain's top zoos. He offered one of their highly trained zoo nurses. A tall, olive-complexioned girl, Mary Collins had a big winning smile and she'd had a fair amount of experience handling big cats, an asset if and when there was a chance of extracting blood and tissue samples from a live King Cheetah.

As to another aspect of the expedition, Paul and I were no strangers to the ''whirr'' and ''click'' of the camera; indeed, we'd had some considerable and not unpleasurable experience of photography during an extensive overland trip through much of New Guinea, Southeast Asia, Indochina and Asia proper some years previously. But, considering the complex nature of the expedition, some practical photographic assistance wouldn't go amiss and to this end we elected to have join us a ruddy-faced, taciturn young man called Steve Downer. By all accounts Steve seemed completely clued up on the technical aspects of photography, especially development. We were, after all, only happy amateurs! Moreover, he possessed a natural reticence that would be a plus factor in working with wildlife, particularly in an area that sees few people.

We also arranged in advance for a first-rate cameraman and sound recordist to fly out to join us in the event of us locating a King Cheetah and capturing it for analysis purposes. Open-dated bookings were duly arranged for them with Sabena and cancellation at any time was deemed no problem.

A request to the Ministry of Home Affairs in Gaborone for a game scout to be seconded to the expedition was granted; but only ten-

Loading up supplies in Gaborone. This was part of a 'modest' donation from Kgalagadi Brewery.

tative arrangements could be managed regarding the services of a cook. It was a matter of seeing to it when we got there, another bit of choice advice would-be "expeditionaries" would do well to remember! Having said that, it is of primary importance to organise as much as possible from homebase, to lay the ground-work, smooth the way so to speak, because if not, it's almost certain that your route through the bureaucratic maze will be severely hampered by red tape. When dealing with government departments in any one of a number of African countries, the absolute autocracy which decides the level of efficiency is beyond the comprehension of the western mind unless experienced at first-hand. In fact, nowhere does that throw-away response, "receiving attention" (as was the case with a number of our permit requests that we'd pre-arranged prior to our arrival) have a more ominous ring! With so much of our planning complete, I took the opportunity of getting in some shooting lessons, deemed wise in the light of where we were going, thus realising a whimsical desire I'd harboured since a child back home in Queensland when I first set eyes on a

45

rifle belonging to my father. Such a natural enthusiasm soon had me reasonably proficient in the use of a ·308, a ·22 and a shotgun, any of which was ideal for our purposes, but as we only required firearms for protection and to shoot-for-the-pot a great armoury of weapons was by no means necessary.

Already an excellent shot, preferring as he does a light rifle, Paul had some brushing up of his own to do, namely his knowledge of Fanagalo. Best described as the lingua franca of southern Africa, this is not an artificially manufactured language like Esperanto, but a simplified form of Zulu, and other related tongues, probably evolved during early contacts between white settlers and black tribesmen and today acting as a bridge between the many idioms spoken right across southern Africa from Namibia and Angola to Mozambique and Malawi.

Departure loomed ever closer as planning shaped and moulded the realities into place till all that remained of major significance was the shipment of our equipment. Counting on securing a good sponsorship deal with a major shipper, as we had been, we were in for a big surprise and I'm not ashamed to admit it!

The sum total of our equipment was considerable, much of it hard-won. Ultimately, getting the expedition off and rolling into the bush without needless delays and unlooked for misfortune depended on us getting that equipment to Africa, intact. Consequently, the warning of "port piracy", reputedly rampant up and down the eastern and western seaboards of Africa, touched a meaningful chord! The adjunct to this? Ship the stuff by container, if, that is, we hoped to see those necessary and hard-won goods of ours reach safe and secure landfall at the other end. The £££ signs multiplied before our eyes. Not that this lessened the possibility of sponsorship; it just heightened the probability of eroding what financial benefits sponsorship brings when set against the overall costs of an expedition. When seeking aid for an expedition it's often true that the greater the cost in real terms of the thing one wants, the weaker it's sponsor potential. Thus, we were playing for high stakes but time would not allow us to deliberate long over sponsorship levels: a ship could take up to six weeks to get to Table

Bay, on top of which there was a stipulated advance booking period to allow time to reserve container space on the sailing of one's choice.

Just twelve short hours before the scheduled delivery of our equipment to the container basin, whence it would eventually begin it's long journey to the bottom of the world, we were due to appear on nation-wide television. Paul was still negotiating with shipping executives at Tilbury when I rolled up at Limegrove studios in "Lulu"... which was promptly deposited in a lift, minus me, and whisked up several stories into the centre of the studio where we were to be interviewed! Impressive stuff for a sweet young colonial! Paul joined me about half an hour later and his face said it all. Our goods were to be shipped at a nominal percentage of the overall price. Fair stood the wind for Africa: the King Cheetah Expedition was launched and on its way!

To where the Swallows go

The flight out of Brussels was laboriously long. By the time I was conscious of being over Africa, the earth-mother itself, our DC-10 had already crossed the equator on it's way south to Kinshasa where we were due to stop briefly to off-load passengers and re-fuel. Glancing down through a porthole window into the interminable pitch below, I could just make out occasional flickers of light on the earth stage, undoubtedly campfires in simple kraals dotted across what was yet an unknown world for me, all of it brilliantly roofed by a classic southern sky crammed full of stars. Southern skies... I'd never realised till then how much I'd missed them.

Just after first light the next morning we touched down at Jan Smuts airport in Johannesburg where the weather was serene, the welcome extended to us by airline staff rousing and hearty. With the VIP treatment came a courtesy car standing by ready to whisk us on our way following the usual Custom's bustle. By comparison, we found a city seemingly devoid of life (which immediately put me in mind of what a prominent British MP once quipped about the city of gold being "closed" on the weekend he arrived!).

Paul and I had flown on ahead well in advance of our team. Apart from organising publicity, following up vital leads and adding to our stores, among other things, there was that ubiquitous, time-consuming business of obtaining government clearances and permits. Consequently, one of our first priorities upon arrival in South Africa—after first seeing to the necessary visitor's papers, import/export permits, etc., as regards that country—was an early trip through to Gaborone. Additionally, we had the considerable task of bringing up the expedition's two Landrovers and remaining equipment overland from Cape Town, where the container ship was scheduled to berth some two weeks after our flight out of the

48

UK. On that day of departure, amid the excitement of publicity stunts, first in the terminal, then again on the tarmac in front of the good ship about to ferry us forth on destiny's wing, our publisher had been full of last-minute talk and instructions about how we should get word back to England quickly in the event of the ultimate occurring. Given the flair for the dramatic we all seemed to have in abundance at that heady time, even the supposedly sacrosanct "diplomatic bag" was mooted as a possibility! In retrospect, even thinking of that possibility was a bit of a cheek. Fortunately, our newspaper sponsor had a correspondent stationed in southern Africa who, we were assured, would get to us at a moment's notice. Be that as it may, he at least offered a reasonably secure outlet for news that, in the part of the world we were heading for, had a habit of going astray.

As regards publicity, press and radio coverage was pretty well instant, the purpose of it being, as far as we were concerned, to foster a public awareness of the King Cheetah and the aims of the expedition, thus eliciting any information that might aid us in some way. Reverberations were even felt as far away as the United States as a result. Generally speaking, however, public knowledge of the King Cheetah was all but non-existent. What did surprise us was how, for the most part (aside from those in some way or another associated with wildlife who pretended otherwise) people welcomed news of a striped cheetah as if it was the revelation they'd been waiting for all their lives! From our point of view, this much was heartwarming at least. In fact, it was from the ordinary person in the street that our press notices attracted the most interesting observations, with one in particular destined to have the most extraordinary repercussions. But that was yet to come. For now, other pressing matters beckoned, like the aforementioned preliminary trip to Gaborone for example.

In size and disposition, Botswana's capital is not much more than a village. It has just two main thoroughfares each flanked by a smattering of one and two-storey buildings leading up to what can be best described as the Botswanan equivalent to Capitol Hill, where the National Assembly and other government buildings

Tuli, north-east Botswana — remote and beautiful country that marked the first area of
field search from base-camp on the Limpopo.

stand in a spacious close. What entertainment exists thereabouts
for both the resident black population and the white community
(which is predominantly made up of diplomatic personnel and
foreign professionals on contract) centres mainly round
Gaborone's two hotels and golf course.

Against such a scenario, considering the wheels had already been
set in motion, in some cases up to six months previously, there
seemed little to prevent us obtaining, in the week-long period we
had set ourselves, all the prescribed Government clearances and
permits necessary to ensure that the King Cheetah Expedition
would get up and start rolling into the bush. But this was Africa,
where no one is in a hurry except you, and where as a result you're
the only one, the product of a time-pressurised society, to end up
with the anxiety neurosis!!

So, despite the delays we encountered as a result of muddle and
mix-up in this or that department—like entire files, including

50

passport papers, references, medicals, being lost completely—the trip was conclusive enough. Of course there were one or two "casualties": Posts and Telecommunications would not permit the use of 2-way radios in the Tuli area because of its proximity to the Rhodesian war, while on a less pressing, more domestic level we didn't manage to obtain the services of a cook for the period (it seems someone had been lined up but was now "otherwise engaged"). I suppose the one benefit of being without a cook was that, in the long run, became quite a dab hand at good bush cuisine.

The camp-kitchen. Lena Bottriell and Game Scout Gulubane.

The appointment of an official Government game scout to the expedition, on the other hand, suffered no setbacks; even permits to transport blood samples went through without a hitch. We managed in the time remaining to address a few interested groups (Rotary for example), to pay our respects to a number of notable dignitaries, to write an article for the country's one and only newspaper, and even to attend a popular cabaret.

One episode, unfortunately, left a sour taste. It was a tale we heard, in passing, at the Department of Wildlife. A German had applied to the Department to come to Botswana to hunt rhino (rare enough there as it is) with a cross-bow and one stipulation: it had to be a three-quarters grown one as the last fully grown rhino he had shot with his trusty cross-bow had taken, so he pointed out with the mindless arrogance of the brutish, four hours to die! Given the doctrinaire stance of certain whites towards the black African's attitude to wildlife, the story, in time, became something of a sick joke.

We found the Botswana Department of Wildlife, though a young department in a relatively young country, to be an enlightened set-up refreshingly aware of it's responsibilities. Indeed it was significant that a licence to shoot-for-the-pot was often harder to get in Botswana than a big-game licence in South Africa. Our chief reason for approaching this department—a request for a game capture permit for the King Cheetah—was granted by the Director. The container ship berthed earlier than expected and within days of leaving Gaborone for South Africa again, we'd been down to and back from Cape-Town with our copious cargo. We had driven the 1400 kilometres right up the centre of the sub-continent through country that offers some of the most breathtaking panoramas of land and sky in all Africa. It all begins in Cape Town, that picturesque city figuratively clinging to the edge of the world. Then it sweeps northwards through lush wine country, thence on to the Karoo, a splendid, vast desert steppe seeming so sublime with it's surrealist vista of mountain, sky and plain—a beauty that reaches down into the soul rather than the kind that pounds the senses into an appreciative numbness—that words convey but the merest hint of it. Driving through in "Lulu", with Paul trail-blazing in "Ingwe", and the setting sun harmonising golden, crimson and violet all along the majestic mesas and buttes that gracefully encircle its sienna expanse, solitude never seemed more natural to the human spirit.

Arriving back in Johannesburg, the weariness put on us by some 18 hours straight driving was quickly dispelled by the excitement of the news awaiting us. An oil company with whom we'd been negotiating had agreed to sponsor the expedition's fuel supplies; we only needed to obtain the necessary permit to carry it in bulk, a standard procedure. But there was something else of quite special significance.

Soon after our arrival in Africa and the first spate of publicity that greeted it, we'd received word about a supposed "colony" of King Cheetahs reputedly living in a secluded area of the war-zone in the remote eastern part of Rhodesia. Having followed it up, we concluded the story had merit and on the strength of this put in a

Gunships, part of a Rhodesian War convoy.

request to the Rhodesian authorities for permission to enter the area in question. A reply was waiting for us on our return from Capetown, the sort of shock reply that it doesn't do to receive too often! A directive from Army Command Headquarters in Salisbury, it exhorted us to come and discuss our requirements with them at our earliest convenience. No eye-witness reports of King Cheetahs were ever to command such attention.

A roads engineer by the name of Waddington had spent some two years with his wife living in a remote area of bush in the dense Pungwe/Honde Valley region of Zimbabwe where he had supervised the construction of a number of roads and bridges. It was during this time, Mrs. Waddington told us, that she and her husband had seen upwards of twenty King Cheetahs, a "colony" of Kings in fact (or as she reverently referred to them by one of their old tags, Royal Cheetah) sometimes singly, sometimes in pairs, occasionally exceeding two but never in the company of ordinary, spotted cheetahs. A gentle woman in her fifties with a face on which experience and the sun had etched a myriad of lines, she confided to us that she had taken her story to a number of museums down the years, but no one had ever seemed much interested, all too often making her feel like some dimwit housefrau who'd spent too long in the bush—a common reaction of museum people to the layman, I regret to say.

The area in question is situated in the Eastern Highlands near the Mozambique border, a region filled with lush vistas of green forest, deep gorges and valleys overflowing with thousands of rushing streamlets that combine to form cascading waterfalls and rivers rich in fish. Indeed, all along the mountain chain, areas of thick to dense bush are interspersed with small, open spaces making perfect havens for secretive, exclusive cats. Significantly this is Manicaland, heart of the *nsuifisi* legend. The Waddington's first sighting occurred at night. They were weaving their way back to camp along a narrow path from one of the construction sites when, caught in the headlights of their truck, their attention was rivetted by two large cats lying in the way. At first they took them to be lions (indeed, in nocturnal bush observation game animals often appear larger than they are). On drawing closer, however, it was the black blotches that made them "stand out, unlike any other animals we had ever seen!". Stopping the vehicle, they sat quietly and watched both of them for some considerable time. Eventually the cats rose and moved off with a slow, nonchalant gait not greatly perturbed, so it seemed to their observers, by the foreign presence so close to them. The cats were doubtless mates and what struck the Waddingtons, as the pair ambled away, was the largeness of what they took to be the male when compared to his mate, although both cats, it was emphasised to us, were bigger than average. Certainly, it was emphasised further, their heads would out-do any normal cheetah for size. It was at this point that Waddington told his wife that he believed they were Royal Cheetahs, or King Cheetahs.

Mrs. Waddington's impassioned comment about how she and her husband had been immediately struck by the black blotches on the animal's flanks is highly significant, this being an outstanding feature of every King Cheetah skin collected. Indeed, the distinctive black blotches stand raised above the background guard hair of the pelage as in a relief or intaglio carving. Also, in describing that first sighting of King Cheetahs at night, plus other sightings after dark that were to follow, the Waddingtons unwittingly echoed a reference from the last century describing a type of cheetah in south-east Africa that was often mistaken at night for "immature lion".

On one occasion, in broad daylight, Mr. Waddington watched a King Cheetah take to water and swim directly upstream, only to emerge some distance up on the opposite bank, shake itself and lurch off into lush undergrowth that at this spot burgeoned almost to the water's edge. While taking to water is known for leopards, it is certainly not a characteristic of cheetahs. As though pre-empting any such thoughts on our part, Mrs. Waddington went on to maintain that there was no possibility of her and her husband confusing the striped cheetahs they saw frequently with leopards, ordinary cheetahs, or for that matter any other cat, notably the smaller striped and spotted serval with which they were familiar. She also stressed that ordinary cheetahs, although fairly common in the vicinity, kept to open country some distance south-west of their camp.

Having given us detailed map references, Paul and I were amazed at the infinite care these people had taken. Experience had shown us that such scrupulous attention to sightings of rare animals does not indicate a tall story. For all its fascination, we also found the information feasible. For one thing it made good sense for King Cheetahs to be forest dwellers, inhabiting remote and thickly vegetated regions, as opposed to the open savanna generally favoured by normal cheetahs. A wooded environment complements the King Cheetah's heavy pelt patterning and longer fur; it would also justify the scarcity of sightings through the decades. Of course King Cheetahs, like any other cats, would wander out of such areas into more open country if advantageous; after all, our fellow animals do not build fences. Unlike modern man, they give vent to their natural instinct to wander with little pre-planning. Leopards, for example, frequently defy the conventions science has thrust upon them, by operating in environments vastly different to the dense cover they are said to favour; and certainly cheetahs don't confine themselves to open grasslands, being known to frequent and in some cases to thrive in woodland and thorn habitat, as in the Kora in central Kenya.

That a so-called colony of the heavily patterned King Cheetah could inhabit one of the densest and most inaccessible parts of Zimbabwe, where one of the longest single-drop falls in the world is to be found, was therefore hardly astounding, but it was a revelation nonetheless. The area around the falls marked the centrepoint of the colony's domain; indeed, according to Mrs. Waddington, a whirlpool at their base was taboo for local Africans. So here we had a remote terrain coupled with primitive superstition. Was this a clue, then, to the secret of the King Cheetah's exclusiveness?

A skin had been collected in this locality some time in the early 1960s, taken supposedly from a young King Cheetah that Waddington had found, treed by some local tribesmen. It seemed unharmed at that stage and on explaining how special the cat was, Waddington entreated them not to harm it. A day or so later, on a visit to their kraal, he was dismayed to find the skin of the cat salted and pegged out to dry in the sun. Because of its rarity he purchased it, then handed it on to the local District Commissioner. That was the last he ever saw of it.

Our reply to Army Command Salisbury was swift and in the affirmative. We were still reeling from the fact that they'd even bothered to consider us, war and all. We would gauge the situation in Tuli first, giving it about a month to six weeks. Then, if things weren't looking particularly optimistic, we'd make a lightning visit through to Salisbury with a view to discussing, on a tentative date, a possible search in the Honde. What we weren't aware of then was that as the Rhodesian war steadily approached it's steamy climax in early 1979, four months hence, the region in question was to fall under strict martial law and would, reputedly, be heavily mined. Hot stuff to say the least! Naturally enough, our Fleet Street sponsors were very nearly beside themselves at the prospect of ourselves and a vet involved in a working study of cheetahs in southern Africa being dropped into a war-zone on the tail of a "colony" of King Cheetahs! Nevertheless, so as not to run the risk of a serious endeavour being turned into some irresponsible, hare-brained stunt, our story was going to have to keep for a while. First we had to make sure that the military was able to offer the support-cover we were going to need.

On the subject of the search in Tuli, things were just not working out regarding the aerial side of the exercise. When it came to the crunch no-one, not even the helicopter firm that had offered help prior to our departure for Africa, was willing to commit a valuable craft for an undefined period of weeks, for an exercise in an area so close to a war-zone. Such misgivings didn't come entirely as a surprise and for our part, in the light of economies alone, were difficult to counter with a sincere heart; the aerial aspect wouldn't come cheap, it had never been argued otherwise. Thus, not to go ahead with it would have changed nothing; the exercise in Tuli, to put it another way, would merely have one less responsibility. The adventuresome spirit takes the good with the bad: it's the only way to fly.

Meanwhile, Mary and Steve arrived and the expedition looked all set to roll. Unfortunately Paul's nephew Kit would not be joining us, as planned, from Rhodesia. In fact he'd already been an invaluable help liaising with Reay Smithers who now, coincidently, was on a two-year's sabbatical research study at the Mammal Research Institute which, naturally enough, happily

Distribution of the
MODERN CHEETAH
Pre-1900

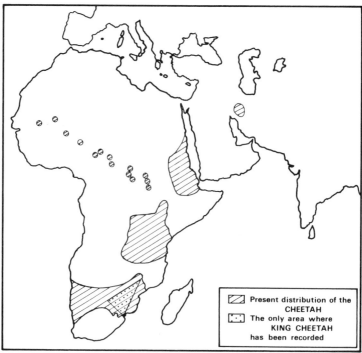

Present distribution of the
CHEETAH

The only area where
KING CHEETAH
has been recorded

58

enabled him to become more directly involved with the expedition. Instead, two South Africans joined the team. Although they had no particular expertise, both were keen wildlife enthusiasts and as such simply joined us in the capacity of "willing helpers" (of which there's never a shortage for expeditions "with-a-difference"). One of them, Keith, had had some limited experience with a game-capture outfit.

It was time to depart for Tuli. On the way through Gaborone we bivouacked to enable the rest of the crew to obtain their individual permits to stay in the country. We were also able to take on a goodly proportion of our food supplies which had been sponsored by a major international hotel chain. To our great relief the chain also acted as news confidant, contact-point, and post office for the expedition throughout its entire thirteen-month stay in Africa. We also received a generous donation of two dozen crates of beer from the local Botswana brewery. Here we stopped to post off reams of special "King Cheetah" postcards, signed by all members of the team, to the children at Bledlow Ridge primary school back in England whose fertile young imaginations had, it seems, fed voraciously on the story of the King Cheetah and our forthcoming expedition when we gave them a talk prior to our departure.

Enthusiasm of the kind these children showed us needs every encouragement, not only to foster a sense of adventure, so vital to the development of the human character, but also to open the way to notions of conservation. The true message of conservation is all too often shrouded in a verbiage born of political expediency and conscience-salving. A charismatic big cat like the King Cheetah (as opposed, let's say, to such droll-sounding creatures as the bald-headed ibis, or the three-toed sloth) cannot help but inspire the right notions.

The distinction, once drawn, between abuse and appreciation is a fine one. I certainly thought so the day we paid our respects at Pretoria Zoo where we were introduced to two rather special VIPs, the white lions of Timbavati fame which had been placed in the confines of the gardens for their own safety, following offers of up to $50,000 for the skin of one! For us, well set upon our determined course to strip away forever from the King Cheetah the anonymity that was its one remaining protector, this take gave us something to think about.

Missionaries' Road

Our journey northward through eastern Botswana to the top-most corner of the Tuli Block, along the old pioneer way, was notable for a sad lack of animal life en route, a scorching reminder of man's ruthless tread through history. It was also useful because it afforded a sterling opportunity to investigate several leads on skins and sightings largely ignored hitherto; and it gave us the opportunity to come across other leads never previously noted in any research.

The reported sightings of two King Cheetahs on a property in the southern Tuli Block as referred to by Smithers in his book *Mammals of Botswana* was, admittedly, only based on hearsay. Nevertheless, it warranted investigation. While in Gaborone, armed with just a farmer's name, we had paid a visit to the Botswana Registry of Lands and Farms, a small office in the Government complex where a charming, smiling Motswana woman looked to have sole charge of the place. This augured well. Just before lunch the same day we received not only the name of the property but its exact map reference as well!

"Stevensford", a large farm covering roughly 44,000 hectares, happened to be situated just across the way from a dusty dot of a place called Machaneng, where the Assistant Game Warden for the district was based, and where, too, Game Scout Phorego Gulubane (reputedly a first class tracker and linguist) was scheduled to meet up with the expedition. In the event of arriving at "Stevensford" in the company of a Government biologist we followed up the reference as best we could. But no one could tell us anything about strangely marked cheetahs having been seen there at any time. Some six months and many miles later, however, the strangest thing happened. A man who had been teaching in Botswana for some years (and who, incidentally, had no reason to know of our investigations at the property in question) told us,

Game Scout Gulubane discussing news of the King Cheetah with a village Headman —
Tuli.

categorically, that he had seen two striped cheetahs running together across an area of land which, on enquiry, he discovered formed part of a farm called.., Stevensford! He neither knew of Smithers, nor of a certain Mr. Challis who was reputedly Smithers' source of information. Such sightings can go on turning up uncannily, again and again, but never amount to anything above what they are—unproved sightings of rare animals.

The same couldn't be said of the flat skin from the store in Lobatse, a small township south of Gaborone. Since that first reference to it prior to our departure, we discovered it had been made up into a lady's jacket; its exact provenance, however, remained unknown. Much, much later, we were to learn its intriguing secret! Equally shrouded in mystery was the provenance of a fine King Cheetah pelt, discovered by Smithers in the possession of a storekeeper in the tiny, one-horse township of Moijabana west of Machaneng; it is now in the collection of the National Museum in Gaborone. It was interesting how, on showing us the skin, the curator opined that the King was more than likely a mutation, one

62

of his reasons for this opinion being that, to the best of his knowledge, the local Africans did not have a specific name for it in their native tongue. We'd wondered about this, too, it being generally held that no name for the King Cheetah existed in any African dialect. We couldn't help but speculate on just how such an opinion had been arrived at, given the King Cheetah's history of neglect, its apparently wide range and the remoteness of its haunts.

By an amazing coincidence, a little over a week later, we met up with an acquaintance from Gaborone on our way through Machaneng. A reliably informed person who had travelled extensively round Botswana because of his involvement in the cattle industry, he told us he had just made the most extraordinary discovery regarding local native names for the King Cheetah. Following soon after an earlier discussion we'd had together on the matter, he had decided to embark on a little investigating of his own and as a result had come up with three strong contenders. One was *lethosi*, described by his African informants as being in some way or other a reference to the "different" cheetah. Another was *tladi*, meaning "lightning". Granted, this latter name was a description one could readily ascribe to cheetahs in general, with obvious reference to their speed; but he had also come across a reference to the ordinary cheetah: *lengau*. Perhaps *tladi* was a discrete reference to the bold flashes extending along the King Cheetah's spine for all to see, or even to its lightning temperament ("cheeky", as opined by tribesmen from time to time). These names brought us no closer to the truth, but they added an intriguing dimension to the King Cheetah story nonetheless.

From one of the consular attachés at the British High Commission in Gaborone—otherwise affectionately known as 007 ½ —we heard tell of yet more skins that had cropped up in research to date. His was a mysterious tale to say the least; indeed a tale of intrigue. In Palapye, a backwater town west of the Tuli Block, there lived a man who at one time or another was said to have owned no less than four King Cheetah skins three of which had "disappeared" in shadowy circumstances. Where they'd supposedly been obtained made the story all the more alluring: they had originated from a skin dealer in Rakops, which is little more than a trading post near the beautiful Boteti river in the dry hinterland of Botswana, west of the Makgadikgadi Salt Pans, those huge, natural, ephemeral "ponds" covering some 12,000 square kilometres in the northern reaches of the Kalahari desert.

This was hardly country one would associate with the King Cheetah. Yet it is as well to remember that in the skin trade, pelts, before actually falling into the clutches of a dealer may travel thousands of kilometres, especially when poached, from their place of collection. In this case, the skins in question could have come from Rhodesia—where cheetahs were classified as "royal game" and as such are protected by law—or even Mozambique. Palapye was only some 100 kms due west of our route north. So, with the rest of the team remaining behind with all our equipment to await the arrival at Machaneng of Gulubane, who had been delayed, Paul and I diverted briefly to Palapye.

The route there resembled the lunar surface following a tremor, covered with sticky red-black, clay-turned-mud in the wake of a recent downpour. Following in the wake of the long, scorching dry season the ground was literally laced with a treacherous network of potholes and ditches that could appear deceptively harmless, until a wheel fell into a ditch, a common occurrence. Dusty and stifling in a pall of heat, Palapye itself impressed one as being like any other obscure township stuck out in the African bush. It was unobtrusive and perhaps just a little shy of strangers, for its economy was dependent upon the few Europeans who had ventured to the area decades before in search of their destiny. The town is primarily a rail-link between Zimbabwe and the south, a tiny eruption of ramshackle buildings huddled close to the tracks as they cut their way clean and crisp across land that lies sparse and flat from horizon to horizon. Indeed, throughout the entire length of the war to the north of Botswana, the line was administered by Rhodesia Railways, although for the benefit of the outside world this sensitive fact was rarely if ever alluded to.

The late Charlie Freeman was one of those Europeans fate had drawn to Palapye years before for one reason or another. An old, unsmiling man when we met him, he was a prominent figure of sorts thereabouts, owning and working, among other ventures, the all-purpose General Store, and the town's one rambling, verandahed hotel where despite the heat the welcome was chilly. Freeman kept his remaining King Cheetah pelt locked away in a safe in his office; it seemed almost a sacrilege. But then I don't think he was much interested in the rights and wrongs of it, the others having been stolen, we must suppose, right from under his

The previously unrecorded King Cheetah skin of the late Charlie Freeman, held by the author outside his store in Palapye in north-eastern Botswana. The one remaining specimen from a reputed collection of four, it illustrates the sheer size of these cats.

nose, thus destroying what was probably a unique collection of its kind in the world.

Living in the dry back of beyond in a place like Palapye, where one may have built up a reasonably comfortable existence from nothing, locals generally endeavour to take outsiders at face value. Thus, when a well-dressed visitor from south of the border dropped in one day at Freeman's store—which did, indeed, appear to be an all-purpose establishment, handling everything from rail shipments to merchandise of every conceivable type—he had no reason, so he told us, to suspect anything untoward. To all intents and purposes, the stranger had come to interview him about his singular set of skins and to photograph it for a southern newspaper. Despite never having gone out of his way to publicise their existence, his suspicions were not aroused, news in the bush having an uncanny knack of travelling! In those days Freeman proudly kept the skins on display in the entrance lobby, allowing them on this occasion to be moved outside where they would photograph better in the daylight. After arranging the skins suitably for their session before the camera, he remembers dashing back inside to attend to some urgent matter and, as he put it, "wasn't gone five minutes". It was within that period, whatever its exact duration, that three pelts vanished and the "photographer" with them. The one still in Freeman's keeping was a superb specimen in excellent condition which he allowed us to photograph and, thereby, to put on record the "Freeman Collection" for the first time. What happened to the other three we cannot say.

Taking our leave of Palapye was no wrench, despite finding what for us was the hub of the town's hospitality, the station office. En route to Palapye the Landrover's roof-rack had taken a severe jolt and had snapped in four places as a result of falling into one of those notorious ditches mentioned earlier; it was essential to have it repaired before tackling the return journey. But we were being wholly frustrated in our attempts to do so, that is until a kindly *Madala* (old man), on learning of our predicament, insisted we let him take us and our problem, to the one "baas who fix things good", the town's white Rhodesian Station-master. Shaking off its miasma of inactivity, the whole town now came alive: suddenly there was fresh tea in bone china cups, home-made biscuits and a madly ingenious, on-the-house repair kit incorporating several hardy, sixfoot gum poles! Here was spontaneous kindness that more than redeemed a sombre Palapye. Our spirits took leave of her all the better for it.

Phorego Gulubane was the son of a chief. On getting back we found him waiting for us a little way out of Machaneng at the camp we'd temporarily set up in the bush. Small of stature, with large horn-rimmed glasses, he had about him an air of scholarship. He certainly looked much older than his supposed "early twenties", although it was out of respect for his person, rather than his age, that we always addressed him as Gulubane and not Phorego. One give-away to his age, however, was his almost unbridled passion for western-style pop music. A first-rate tracker, as we were to discover for ourselves, with excellent English and a peerless sense of fun, "Gulues" — as Paul was wont to call him—was to prove a boon companion in more ways than one.

We headed north to Zanzibar. Zanzibar? Ahhh... long have I cherished the desire to travel to Zanzibar, that exotic-sounding isle off the coast of Africa, once-upon-a-time haven for salty buccaneers and Arab caiques. But ours was not the Zanzibar of romantic legend. No coral beaches or musk-ridden markets pungent with the aroma of cloves awaited where we were heading. An arid, sweltering spot with not even the remotest pretension to palm-studded beauty, our Zanzibar was little more than a pin-prick on the map of Botswana, a turn in the road where not much besides a petrol pump and an empty hotel marked its presence. Its reason for being—and our reason for giving it a second glance— was a ranch of the same name whose owner, we'd heard tell, possessed another unrecorded King Cheetah skin.

Laurens Van Niekerk is something of a rarity among white ranchers in this part of the world, having for the past thirty-five years lived permanently at Zanzibar like his father before him. Others, like the grazier further south who'd offered us an area of land where we could temporarily release a King Cheetah—in the event

This previously unlisted King Cheetah skin belonging to Mr Laurens Van Niekerk was collected in the Tuli region and photographed at his Zanzibar Ranch, north-eastern Botswana.

of our capturing one—so that we could carry out our intended tests and studies, mostly divided their time between their ranches and interests elsewhere. His King Cheetah skin was a well-cured pelt in beautiful condition, reputedly collected in the late sixties on the perimeter of the Tuli Circle, thus giving credence to those reports we'd had, of skins and sightings alike, from the area.

As for the skin, Van Niekerk had paid a hawker a mere £1 10s for it, although he'd been offered about £2000 for it since! The man was no big-game hunter; one had only to cast an eye around the homestead to know that. It was, therefore, with some concern that he told us of the alarming level poaching had reached in eastern Botswana with most of it being carried out on a large scale from across the Limpopo. He cited examples personally known to him of crossings being made under cover of darkness. Unfortunately, a desperate shortage of trained personnel and proper resources in secluded areas of open bush doesn't permit effective, long-term, preventative measures against this kind of poaching, especially sophisticated operations. Examples of simple rural villagers adding something extra to their meagre diet of mealies present no problem. In many instances, the poachers cross the border in four-wheel-drive vehicles, set a compass bearing and drive for all they are worth, shooting everything on sight, taking only the hind-quarters if biltong (wind-and shade-dried meat) is their desire, more if skins and horns are wanted as trophies. Sometimes government game scouts on scrambler bikes in hot pursuit of a truckload of these poachers must suddenly skid to a standstill to avoid trails of spikes scattered in their path. Shades of Hollywood indeed!

Of course, cynics will argue that the trouble with countries like Botswana is that the laws controlling poaching are too lax; moreover, the people themselves neither understand nor give a hoot about so-called game conservation. But this kind of sweeping, facile argument holds up less and less as more countries in Africa come to rely on tourism as an increasingly important source of national income and employment, appreciating the enormous financial potential that lies with preserving and responsibly promoting the wonderful legacy they have inherited for nothing. One

Wild lilies adorn the banks of the Limpopo looking upstream towards the Mashatu camp. The river, here only half-full at the onset of the rainy season, is a formidable obstacle when in full flood, completely cutting access to Botswana from the Transvaal.

should consider that almost the entire population of Botswana was totally dependent on hunting for its food and other requisites until very recent times. In the so-called civilised world, on the other hand, hunting as a need and as a general free-for-all was eradicated centuries ago. The present level of understanding in Botswana as to what conservation is all about is admirable, given how long it has taken many "better-off" nations to reach the same stage! Nonetheless, it was sad to hear Paul comment on the scarcity of game as we moved northward into Tuli. He told me that even some ten years previously, driving along a bush trail in this part of the world could be hazardous on account of the variety of animals darting across one's path. Nowadays, in parts of Africa, it can be like travelling through a void, so much has the game been shot out. Why, as recently as the 1960s, there were areas in Botswana where reputedly upwards of one hundred zebra a day were being slaughtered for their skins. Thus, Paul's descriptions of

70

herds of game congregated in their thousands were almost impossible to visualise. Later on, when I did see herds of up to a thousand zebras, wildebeest and impalas, something of those glorious images of an Africa past he had been trying to paint for me came alive at last.

Northward out of Zanzibar on the last leg of our journey, the route deteriorated rapidly making the going tediously slow and uncomfortable. Heavily laden as we were, with some valuable equipment on board, it was as much in our interests to take things carefully as it was for the wildlife thereabouts. It is always unwise to drive at speed through the bush (regardless of the state of one's route of passage be it track or open terrain) this being the way many an unfortunate animal gets killed. Thus, it was a slightly frayed convoy—not entirely full of the joys of spring you might say—that wearily plodded its way on through the heat and dust of a sticky, tropic afternoon. We were making for the one remaining port-of-call in our search for unrecorded skins before the final push to that corner of paradise huddled close to the Shashe/Limpopo confluence, our destination. Our journey took us into the Talana Estates where the landscape took on a decidedly lush appearance after the patchwork of scrub country we'd just come through.

Seemingly the last outpost of civilisation, the "Estates" was a sizeable chunk of lush plantations in an ocean of bush notable for one other reason; it boasted a store, "Red Shields", which had given its name to a King Cheetah skin, all trace of which had since been lost. Again echoing those reports we'd received while still in the UK, the skin, reputedly collected at some stage in the late sixties/early seventies near the Tuli Circle, remained for a number of years in the possession of the store's former owner. Neither at this stage, however, nor again later were we able to learn any more than what we already knew about the Indian store-owner, or the mysterious skin which has come to be called "The Red Shields skin".

Perhaps this skin was connected in some way with the talk of the two skins, also supposedly collected in the area, that had acquired the dubious distinction of apparently being auctioned in "South

Africa somewhere''. Rumours of another King Cheetah pelt pinned up on the wall of a homestead just up the way added further to the speculation. But the recent passing of laws—not before time, either—forbidding the procuring of ''spotted skins'' (into which loose category King Cheetahs fitted) outside of designated hunting concessions was doubtless having a good effect. With Gulubane present in his capacity of Government Game scout (if the occasion necessitated it, he wore his uniform) subsequent investigations at the farm drew a complete blank. No one interviewed was keen to discuss any cat skin, no matter how long before the new laws it had been collected, and where!

We passed on to the Motloutse River, cutting it's transitory course down to the great, grey-green, greasy Limpopo immortalised by Kipling. At once a whole new vista opened up before us. Most rivers in Botswana, apart from the Zambezi, the Okavango and about three other major watercourses, are ephemeral. The Motloutse was one such, being for as far as the eye could see in either direction, completely dry. Thus, loaded down as we were, crossing it's 200 metres width was not without it's complications, the Landrover's heavy 8-ply tyres, under the pressure of all the weight, cutting deep furrows through the soft sandy bed as though it was made of marshmallow. From here on the vegetation changed dramatically. A rich riverine landscape danced ahead of us, lush green groves of wild fig trees... silver-trunked and shiny-leaved, doum-palms, mlalas and exotic euphorbias all emerging where there had only been stubby mopane before. Thorn trees, scattered here and there seemed taller and stronger while elsewhere lacey, flat-topped acacias—for some the essence of Africa—edged the skyline like fretted doilies.

Although there were traces of trodden and chewed mopane where elephants had left their mark, majestic stands of tall mopane woodland made an appearance along the river, as did the lovely yellow-barked acacia, or fever tree, so called by early pioneers because of it's association with malaria. The pallid colour of its trunk, as if just painted with yellow gouache, doubtless encouraged the belief; the later-discovered prevalence of malaria mosquitoes

Paul Bottriell at a vantage point overlooking the Majale River in Tuli. The area, stretching in a triangle from Tuli to Crocodile River in the eastern Transvaal up to the Highlands of eastern Zimbabwe, is typical of the type of wooded terrain associated with the King Cheetah.

along watercourses that fever trees favour explained it. Popular look-outs for leopards, many of the fever trees around Tuli were to be found clinging to the gnarled faces of high kopjes hugging watery tracts. For me, the whole area had the feel and look of the Africa of old I'd only been able to imagine.

The physical lay of the land, too, took on a vastly different character from the Motloutse onwards. Where before the vehicles had been grappling with indentations instead of tracks, now only sheer rock beckoned us onwards. And in a Landrover that's no fun! The only real way to operate in the open bush is, of course, on foot. Vehicles and anything beyond a game trail are quite simply out-of-keeping with the wild's own inimitable rhythm and pace.

We pitched camp on the edge of the Limpopo, for the most part barren of water, for it was the time of year when Botswana is at its hottest and driest, before the rains. With the onslaught of the wet season, predominantly in December and January just a few

73

months hence, rivers that are little more than parched drains in the dry season can come to be in spate. For now, however, there was just a dry, cavernous void where our camp immediately overlooked the Limpopo... although, ironically, it was in full flow "on the other side"!

The Limpopo forms a natural border between Botswana and South Africa and as it flows through both countries it can be simultaneously empty of water on one side while in flow on the other, a central bank or finger-shaped "island" marking the dichotomy between two wide channels. The camp itself was situated in a clearing on an otherwise densely vegetated escarpment, or bank, that rose to about ten metres above the river-bed and afforded a clear view for some distance up and down the river. The rich riverine landscape flanking it sported some magnificent tree forms, while all around us the undergrowth was lush and heavily overgrown. As such it offered some welcome refreshment for the eye and psyche alike on days when temperatures soared, without even the slightest possibility of a river breeze bringing some solace. But while creating a welcome illusion of coolness, this attractive oasis of greenery also offered sanctuary to numberless snakes and lizards.

In a cleared area we set up home underneath the hospitable spread of a huge and venerable mashatu tree. The odd assortment of sitting tenants, included an inquisitive, three-foot long water monitor lizard, making for all-round camp entertainment. Disconsolately scattered about were several pairs of antelope horns, a hulking elelphant skull (which along with the pelvic bone of the same beast made for an excellent seat and coffee table) a monkey skeleton, and the skull of what was very likely the last rhino in Tuli to be shot. The campsite also boasted a large "ant-hill", or termite mound, one of those magnificent eruptions of earth built up round the royal chamber of the queen by generations of termites, a remarkable citadel of fungus gardens, vegetable storage chambers, air-shafts and passages to the outside. This one, a healthy eight-footer of ten to fifteen years standing, sprouted overnight picturesque mushrooms the size of dinner plates. When the rains came the

Lena and Paul Bottriell game-viewing on a bank above the Limpopo. There was always something to be seen, from elephant to bushbuck in search of water.

nuptial evening flight of the winged "alates", future kings and queens, from out of the mound was something remarkable to see At one end a large tarpaulin, strung up over the trees and hanging down on the windward side to provide protection while remaining open elsewhere, offered alternative sleeping quarters, the stores being split between one of the tents and the caravan "photo-lab". It was from here that another, larger, tarpaulin measuring some fifteen by twenty feet was strung out to form a kind of galley under which a convenient makeshift bench was formed making use of a long branch of the mashatu that ran prostrate along the ground. With cooking utensils arranged accordingly, the camp-kitchen was thus born. Indeed, it was within such rustic surroundings that many a tasty dish was also born; where, too, one learned through continual experimentation to prepare game meat, notably impala, employing a variety of ways for cooking over the open fire. The method that suited us best (with what "gourmet" ingredients we had to hand) was to marinate, at the first opportunity a day ahead of time, fresh slices of meat in a mixture of onion rings, tomato puree and beef stock generously seasoned with garlic salt, allspice and a good dash of Worcester Sauce. Come dinner time in the evening, the whole concoction would be transferred to a plough-disc set up over the open fire—a simple but ingenious method that insures meat is cooked carefully rather than too rapidly—where the slices of impala meat would poach gently in the same highly-flavoured marinade. It also made up into an excellent stew and could be set over the fire in a three-legged pot for hours with no supervision.

The fire was, of course, the heart and soul of the camp—our hearth if you like. Strategically placed in the centre, it offered an all-round aspect of bush and river, at the same time allowing plenty of space to spread out. It was a most beautiful camp in a beautiful setting, highlighted by the autumnal-hued Egyptian geese that each even-ing, just before sundown, would fly north up the Limpopo towards Rhodesia, the long, piercing cries of their passage identifying them long before they could be seen. Indeed, though in flow elsewhere along the Botswana stretch of river, from where the camp overlooked it the Limpopo was well and truly just a wide hollow of soft, dry sand, multi-coloured pebbles and pearly shells... yet we wouldn't have had it any other way. The game trails that led down onto the riverbed just below and over across the sands to the island and the water beyond it, brought a daily spectacle to our Eden—the panorama, towards late afternoon, of game in droves coming down to drink.

Impalas—lithe, athletic antelopes, just a little larger than the big-ger gazelles—were always the most numerous. With their rusty gold coats glinting in the sunlight, the handsome lyre-shaped horns of the bucks bobbing upwards and backwards, these nimble-heeled creatures of the aesthetically pleasing line and high flying leaps— the best in all Africa—would nip gracefully across the sand in orderly files, calmly and purposefully in step. By contrast, those dainty vervet monkeys, so like little grey clowns with tiny energetic faces like black masks, would dash about in excited dozens chatting incessantly; likewise parties of banded mongoose that came and went, though slightly less hysterically.

Dappled, chocolate-coated, Limpopo bushbuck would shyly peer from quiet cloisters along the river just below the camp. Even these would fall prey to cheetah.

Occasionally, dappled chocolate bushbucks would peer from their sheltered green cloisters near the water and wander tentatively by the camp. These were Limpopo bushbucks, one of forty or more races of bushbuck whose bambi-like beauty belies a most formidable nature. Stealthy, usually solitary creatures, they shun the company of man. The waterbuck, on the other hand, one of the bigger varieties of antelope, without whose appearance the tableau would never be quite complete, is somewhat more tolerant, though shy nonetheless. An animal of quiet, singular dignity decked out in a coat of grey, the sight of it never failed to thrill me. The water-buck of south-east Africa sports a shaggy hide with a large white ellipse stencilled dramatically across its rump, a softly-falling

77

collar-like mane partially framing a serene face that has none of the blankness of expression peculiar to some species of antelope and gazelle; and the bull has long "hunting-trophy" horns in the shape of a wishbone. In the harsh reality of the bush, such is what places the waterbuck among the loveliest sights a person can encounter. The news that we had only few crocodiles as near-neighbours came as a bit of a shock. Equally disturbing was our discovery that the giraffe had suffered much the same fate as the rhino. Elegant wild creatures of the long necks and languorous eyes, giraffes principally represented to early pioneers moving north in their ox-wagons the source of the longest, complete leather band in the world; so they were mercilessly shot out to make reins and whips. Eastern Botswana has an intriguing recent history. In the latter half of the nineteenth century, the fertile Tuli strip marked the only proven route from the Cape to the wild northern interior, via Fort Macloutse and Fort Tuli. Known as the English, or Missionaries' Road, it was trod by explorers and hunters, adventurers and pioneers such as Livingstone, Selous and Rhodes. The area designated on maps as the Tuli Block originated as a result of Rhodes's plan for a Cape-to-Cairo railway. A concession was granted to the British by Khama, the paramount chief of the Bechuana, for a strip of land running parallel to the Limpopo all the way from Mafeking in the south to the Shashe River in the north, on the condition that the area be settled by the British and their allies so as to form a buffer against Boer expansion. The railway line scheme itself foundered on geography and the line was re-routed further inland, where it remains today—good news it could be said for what has remained, in part at least, a demi-paradise.

A short distance downstream from our camp stood one of the tallest trees in the area, a magnificent giant mashatu under which Rhodes pitched his tent and bided a few months on his way north (his initials are carved on the bark). Here too, in the 1890s, a tiny settlement sprang up, marked today by little more than a forgotten, overgrown trail leading down to the river which would then have teemed with croc and hippo alike. It was at this point (known

The author, Mashatu camp. It was previously the site of a
big-game hunters camp, as the kudu horns and elephant skull
in the background sombrely attest.

appropriately as Rhodes Drift for reasons that will become clear)
that pioneer columns en route to Fort Tuli would portage heavily-
laden wagons across the Limpopo in a highly ingenious way. They
would let them drift across with the down-current, guided, one by
one, by a rope strung from a wagon to a tree situated some distance
upstream on the opposite bank. In plucky disregard of the crocs

79

and hippos, a strong swimmer would retrieve the rope after each crossing ready for another haul.

As for the crocodiles, they are no longer numerous enough to keep the species thriving in Tuli. Unlike the unprecedented return of the elephant to the area in the 1950s there is little hope of such a renaissance of *Crocodylus niloticus*; not only is, it not "nomadic" in the sense the elephant is, it faces the added problem of having a very limited habitat these days. There are few major rivers and bodies of water in Africa that man hasn't encroached upon or fished out. Another problem is the savage predation of croc's eggs by mongooses, monitors, baboons and the like. Neither can the scourge of poaching be forgotten. Love them or hate them, crocodiles also have their place in nature's magic cycle of life, everything being interdependant. They aren't the most lovable creatures on offer in the wild—approximately ten people a day in Africa are dragged off to an end too horrible to contemplate... and these are only the ones we know about!—but when you've been around as long as they have, virtually unchanged for 150 million years, then you deserve an unequivocal right to a continued place in nature.

A favourite hunter's story that illustrates yet another side to the crocodile problem tells the tale of a student who received a grant to travel to the Okavango in north-west Botswana, a vast, magnificent inland-delta basin of marshes, rivers, lagoons, channels and islands, making it one of the world's greatest remaining natural wildlife preserves where nomad and game predominate. Here he was to undertake the field-work for a thesis on the eating habits of *Crocodylus niloticus*. The result was the mass slaughter of about a thousand crocs! Fortunately there is still a future for the Nile crocodile, bleak as that may be in Tuli, thanks to serious breeding programmes in southern Africa aimed at ultimate re-introduction to the wild. There are places in Africa, wild places, where the croc is doing very well, as it is in the Luangwa Valley of Zambia where they number untold thousands, reputedly the largest aggregation of crocodiles on the African continent, or maybe anywhere else. Thus, on our stretch of the Limpopo, we may not have counted amongst our nearest neighbours the venerable, voracious saurians. A big, beautiful, be-whiskered bachelor leopard we certainly did. A splendid bronzed tom of immaculate proportions, he lived some three hundred metres away, along the approach to the camp amongst the rocks and crags of a long, narrow kopje that also offered stony sanctuary to several dozen rock hyraxes (or rock rabbits), the smallest of the hoofed mammals and reputedly the closest living ungulate relatives of the elephant. He was a wily character and clearly one not used to having people around. For all that, however, we glimpsed and heard him often, nocturnal visits to the camp being among his surprise specialities.

One episode that occurred during daylight is written indelibly in my memory. At the time I was typing up the log of events to date, sitting comfortably in a deck-chair under the shade of the spreading mashatu overhanging the camp, my portable typewriter in my lap. Paul and Gulubane, meanwhile, were some distance away manfully tackling the highly odorous task of blowing half a dozen ostrich eggs found abandoned by their mother in a flooded vlei (a type of grassy hollow, or meadow, that turns swampy in the rainy season). No one else was around. It was noon—siesta time in the wild—when everything in Africa seems at peace with the world. Suddenly, the lazy torpor of day was shattered by a savage, blood-curdling stridor of animal cries that rose up out of the jungle-growth a few metres away from me. I froze. Amid the tuneless cacophony of resonant, bellowing barks typical of dog baboons when excited, and the chilling, hysterical screams of younger ones, an unmistakeable gurgling sound filtered through: a baboon was dying... and transcending it, the short, sharp grunts of a leopard. I didn't need to see it. Astride a tree limb where doubtless it would have bolted with the dying baboon, steel jaws gripping its victim's neck like a vice, the big bronzed cat would be holding its own before a murderous phalanx of baboons screaming revenge; with each grunt the leopard sounded a fair warning. One slip, and those formidable enemies of the leopard might have him. But the bronzed beast would have been well in control; a return visit from him a day or so later confirmed it. We didn't see any baboons around the camp again for quite some time after that, although the troupe lived just across the river where their arrogant comings and goings often attracted our eye. Despite that near encounter everything was just as it should be. Home on the Limpopo remained the most magic spot in all the world.

On the Edge of Everywhere and Nowhere

The task of searching out a live King Cheetah, this feline rara avis, began in earnest within days of pitching our tents. We were now six, Keith being unable to remain with the expedition as he'd hoped and having taken his leave of us shortly after our arrival in Tuli—or, rather, Mashatu as the particular area where we'd made base-camp came to be romantically known. We aimed to contain the search within an area of roughly 1000 square kilometres, a triangle of land between the Shashe and Limpopo Rivers, utilising two Landrovers and splitting the team accordingly. The motors were considered merely as a means of transportation from one place to another, not as search vehicles.

Breaking camp soon after dawn, we would drive in separate parties to designated areas to spend the best part of a morning well-placed on a look-out (a high ridge or kopje or other like prominence) surveying the surrounding bush with a pair of strong binoculars, while also going walkabout before temperatures soared to inhospitable heights (at their worst between eleven and three) which, in bush-work, is so hazardous to health and performance. In setting out to relate here the circumstances of our day-to-day physical search of bushland country, I find myself confronted with a problem: do I just say that we went out into the bush every day and looked for a King Cheetah? I could, if I was simply telling the story of the King Cheetah. I'm not, however, simply telling that story but rather the story of the *quest* for the King Cheetah, which means telling something about the incidents and pitfalls, joys, highlights and perplexities of the constantly changing cir- cumstances that go to make up any quest involving challenge and adventure, chance and the joy of being alive. Certainly the "needle in a haystack" syndrome applied. Distractions abounded. That's what a quest is all about. There would be nothing to tell otherwise.

After all, we were in Africa, haven of so much that is beautiful, unexpected or treacherous, of nature's making, or man's.

On outward journeys to a chosen destination, laden with camera, various lenses and binoculars, we took to riding on the roof of the Landrover while one or other of us manned the helm and steered us on a steady course through the open bush. It was one means of spotting and photographing animals at close quarters that we adopted while moving about by vehicle. For surprise, stealth and absolute manoeuvrability, however, it could never quite replace the footpatrol.

Our two parties operated on a rota system between various look-outs, there being particular ones that afforded viewing on a vast scale. At one such vantage point enjoying a view over an expansive plain where cheetahs and elephants roamed, herds of zebra, impala and wildebeest in their hundreds could be seen almost any day mingling with clusters of shyer kudu and eland. The greater kudu's majestic, spiralling horns are much coveted by hunters, while the Cape eland, taller by almost a foot with both sexes bearing short horns like great fat screws is, despite its massive size (standing up to six feet at the withers and often weighing as much as a ton), shy of even distant humans. A remarkably high jumper, it can clear metres-tall obstacles. A migrating herd of eland a couple of hundred strong, is quite a sight.

The terrain became considerably more open and dryer and the vegetation less lush the further into Tuli one ventured. From the rich riverine landscape of wild figs, stately mashatus, lustrous euphorbias (or candelabra trees, so-called because of the way they hold up their branches to the sun in ritual homage), vines and tall mopane woodland that courted the Limpopo and Shashe rivers, the country between thinned out dramatically into tracts of gnarled mopane scrub, the tree's growth checked to only a few metres height by elephants which feed on the foliage and bark. Further on again the plains opened out, granting a haven to Tuli's large herds of game. Providing welcome adornment to the plain profile of the land were buffalo thorn trees, occasional patches of tall mopane woodland dancing round the edges of some river or vlei, a ridge

84

The wildebeest has a grace that belies its image. The bull of this herd was convinced we had covetous designs on his ladies, and whenever we appeared would spend much of the time, in between challenging our presence so close to the herd, rounding them up and herding them along.

of cragged and fretted kopjes, an ant-hill, and even a monstrous baobab—the legendary cream-of-tartar or "upside-down tree".

Once, for the best part of a couple of hours late one afternoon, during a stint on a look-out, we became the objects of fascination for a change. A lone bull wildebeest, from his "sentry post" some twenty or so metres below us, kept up a tireless vigil of noisy scrutiny as he snorted and pawed the ground impatiently in mock challenge to our presence so close to the herd. This one merely amused us, but a mature wildebeest bull can prove to be a formidable adversary when really alarmed. There have been cases when one of these quite ineffectual-looking rogues has kicked in the front of a four-wheel-drive vehicle, doubtless considered by the wildebeest to have had covetous designs on his ladies.

The controversial guerilla war to the north was rapidly escalating when we visited the "place-where-three-nations-meet" for the first time. For all that, here at the confluence of the Limpopo and

Shashe Rivers, we might just as well have been standing on the moon, so little did we sense the feverish pitch and toss of war just over the way. It was as though we'd stumbled onto a lush fragment of Shangri-la where the only obvious sign of life was a school of hippos wallowing about joyfully in water that was nothing like the usual murky brown of African rivers, but as crystal clear as a highland stream. A secluded sanctuary of sublime beauty, to get to it we first had to make our way on foot through a couple of kilometres of verdant jungle on what was a kind of island in the very centre of the confluence itself. Brimming over with rich tropical growth from lianas to snakes, it gave way to scenery of a totally different nature. Where we stood, on the very tip of Botswana, all was dank and green. To our right, just across the Limpopo in South Africa, a jagged, imposing line of rust-coloured kopjes hugged the waterline, while straight ahead of us immediately over the Shashe, a pale white-beached inlet sat cosily between two burnished bronze cliffs towering majestically into a cloudless, azure sky. It was almost more than I could bear not to shed my boots and splash on ahead across the sapphired shallows of what was the Shashe—this so-sensitive border—to the soft, tranquil sands opposite where nothing stirred save the tasselled clumps of dune grass fringing it. Paradoxically, never before or since have I happened upon a place of more perfect peace.

Just around the back of the island in the dried-up channel, or "false river" that links the Limpopo with the Shashe, we surprised a sounder of bushpig. Catching what could have only been the slightest sense of us, they took off like bolts of grounded lightning across the long stretch of sand marking the bed of the channel, their hoofed feet hardly seeming to touch the ground which in places was so soft and yielding underfoot that one could barely move without sinking into it ankle deep. The bushpig's principal predators are leopards and lions. Consequently, they are far from cowardly and will, if needs be, defend their young bravely, turning their not insubstantial tusks—which are really long canines—against any attacker, whether cat or man.

There was reputedly a very hostile lioness resident in the area . On

86

one occasion we were sure we were about to make her acquaintance rather sooner than we would have liked! A sharp, meaningful grunt at no less than loudspeaker distance but seemingly just inches from our ears, suddenly stopped us dead in our tracks. That cold, tingling pins-and-needles feeling clings to you still, long after you learn that the virago in the bushes you thought was a big cat is a big, bad dog baboon playing the ape!

In thick bush country, good landmarks are as much a bonus as a stout pair of desert boots is for walking. Thus where we'd been forced to leave the Landrover and continue on foot, a terraced, steep-faced tower of a kopje looming straight up out of the verdant mantle of jungle like some majestic ziggurat, made a most convenient marker. Right at the top of this rocky shrine, some eighty feet up, a weathered old African, like some primitive ascetic, had carved out of the rock a simple home, a home that, by virtue of the setting over which it had dominion, was indeed a castle! Otherwise, in keeping with its aura of seclusion, Tuli had few inhabitants.

We'd already paid our respects to the only tribe to speak of in the area, an activity that warrants mention because it illustrates beautifully the value of serendipity without which research would be much the poorer. In the course of conversation with the chief, a rake-thin, snowy-haired old gentleman of indeterminate years, the source of our interest, the King Cheetah—the ''different cheetah'' if you like—was referred to by him not once, but several times as *Lethosi*. Coincidence? Who's to say? It seems to me that our most fervent thoughts, like subconscious wishes, have the knack of giving life where there seems none.

Just west of Tuli, behind its so-called ''back-line'', lay a vast tribal territory purged of game, having been given over, in the way of so many developing countries in Africa, to the cattle grazing that represents the greatest threat to its wildlife. The first time we ventured into the territory, dropping in at some of the cattle kraals within striking distance of Tuli, our arrival seemed to occasion some delight among the villagers. It seems that a local prophet had foretold our coming; shortly after, we received the first bit of

British Natural History Museum's mounted King Cheetah. Note the similarity to Leopard in the way it has been mounted.

worthwhile news on the King Cheetah since making our camp on the Limpopo.

In the winter of the previous year, an African tracker had seen what he'd later come to believe was a King Cheetah at a spot in amongst mopane bush roughly ten kilometres cross-country from our base. At a loss at the time to know what it was, he spoke little of the incident to anyone, his argument being that "no-one would believe him"! On meeting Joseph for the first time, one got the impression of someone who knew his game well as he described what had happened. On a clear morning, through a clearing

Mounted specimen of a King Cheetah. Cape Town Museum, South Africa.

between some scattered trees, a cat crossed his path near enough for him to take particular note of the bold, distinctive stripes running along its back. Judging it to be heavier than a cheetah, he watched as it hurried off in the direction of a stream.

Be they hunters, game management personnel or naturalists, we'd frequently shown such people photographs of the stuffed King Cheetah specimens housed in the Natural History Museum in London and in the Cape Town Museum. There is a marked difference between the two specimens in the way each has been mounted: the former resembles a leopard with stocky legs, heavy neck and head, no doubt mounted under the influence of the notion popular around 1927 that the King Cheetah might be a hybrid leopard/cheetah; the Cape Town Museum's King Cheetah, on the other hand, was mounted later and bears a greater resemblance to a cheetah because of the way it has been modelled. What was interesting about Joseph's reaction to the photographs was that he was the only person up to that time to spot the difference between the two, derisively brushing aside the "British" King with the comment that it "was not a leopard" that he saw "but a cheetah with stripes and blotches like the one in the other photograph!". How unfortunate he didn't report the sighting straightaway! Apprehension got the better of him it would seem. Such an attitude, I'm afraid, often finds root in another equally negative attitude: the habit of a great many whites to denigrate such an observation because of what they claim is the African's "tendency to embroider". Attitudes of this kind die hard. As a result, a large percentage of leads on the rare and unusual are not reported or are simply lost somewhere between doubt and distrust, those great dividers of mankind.

It was November and the rains arrived with a vengeance. Harbingers of more to come after New Year, what tracks we'd made in and around Tuli were completely awash within hours of the deluge. When the rain finally abated, three days later, only thick, oozing mud remained in their stead. Indeed, it was over this period that we were subjected to the estimated total annual rainfall of the area, an onslaught that nearly saw the entire camp swept away down the timeless reaches of the Limpopo.

The elephants should have been enough warning for us. Just after nightfall, while the camp was preparing for dinner, Gulubane decided to take a short stroll. There was an atmosphere of calm that betrayed nothing of the fury yet to be unleashed. Shortly afterwards, a bright light could be seen through a black veil of bush bobbing hurriedly towards the camp. It dipped and jogged in a most agitated fashion like some giant, frenzied firefly dancing about on the tree-tops as it came nearer. Except for the glow thrown up by the fire, the night was pitch black, as nights are in the bush, visibility in the surrounding area being largely reduced. A powerful beam like that of a search-light, so totally unexpected in it's intensity that it blinded us temporarily, burst suddenly upon our faces as from out of the darkness beyond came the strained cry "JUMBO!". We recognised Gulubane's voice. Moments later, when our eyes had focused again, we noted that our game scout had achieved the seemingly impossible—he had turned white with fright! Little wonder, for less than fifty metres from the edge of camp he had walked straight into a herd of foraging elephants. They may be the biggest land animals around but you can be standing within feet of one ambling through the bush and not hear a twig snap! Footloose elephants so close to camp were unusual and spelt one thing: they were restless, doubtless sensing the approach of what was soon to overwhelm us.

About half an hour later a stiff breeze blew up. We thought little of it; we had little chance. Before anyone could count ten we were locked in a furious battle with the elements, a termagant of wind and rain suddenly lashing the camp. Who, when unprepared for it—and couched in however colourful a language—can adequately describe the wrath of a tropical storm! With no time to spare the choices were simple. Our first priority was to secure the tents as well as we could and then to save the stores. We managed both, despite the opposition. We saved our wood supply and managed to sling up a protective canvas over the fire, thus saving what was left of it. We ate late that evening.

By midnight, the worst of it had died down. With the coming of first light it had ceased altogether; so, thankfully, had the noise. Like a monotonous one-note samba, a tuneless fugue for strings, it had played along with the wind and the rain (as if we needed the mood to be set for us!). Now, with the lull morning brought, peace reigned again over the bush. To appreciate the unpredictability of Nature's moods, however, we didn't have to be reminded of the night's events; one glance around was enough, nature's cataclysms being very untidy. The respite was short-lived. Later that day the rains returned in earnest, though less frenetic in the manner of their coming, and continued non-stop for two whole days, leaving us little choice but to keep to camp. At last they blew themselves out and there followed two or three days of blue skies and sunshine. Still the sludge remained in many parts, hardly surprising after the torrential drenching the earth had been given, leaving the ground dangerously slippery in places for both foot and wheel. It is in conditions of this nature in the bush that a vehicle as heavy as a Landrover can get bogged down to its axles. Old vehicle tracks cutting across open bush ground, deep and stubbornly refusing to dry out, after heavy, soaking rain, are particular hazards; moreover, they can be an even greater threat, especially in an emergency situation, when they have dried out. Some tracks, deeply incised in the ground up to ten inches and more and baked rock-hard by the sun, may cause havoc if one's wheels drop into them. Then there were elephant tracks, large, round pug-prints up to five and six inches deep in ground dried hard as concrete. We didn't drive over them, we bounced over them! They were a different matter altogether when wet.

Frequently, one would come upon game trails littered with the left-overs of elephant feasts, twigs and branches, the jumbo's "hors-d'oeuvres" which we referred to affectionately as "lolly-sticks". During the wet, however, it wasn't only the "I was here" lolly-sticks they left behind, but the aforementioned large, round and generally muddy incisions in the soft earth where they had trod a purposeful path along a game trail or vehicle track. Needless to say, falling flat on your back into such a mire is a chastening event "friends" and associates do not allow you to forget. By the time I'd squelched and jerked, stiff-limbed, the four or five kilometres back to camp in the heat of the day, feeling like the tin-man, my joints had seized up completely, the mud coating them having dried in the sun to something resembling cement!

But with the rains there came compensations. It was as if nature had had a face-life, with the land and it's offspring wilfully growing anew. The grass shot up fresh-green and lush by inches, while, more spectacularly, the trees of the area distended round the entire circumference of their bole, or trunk, by as much as up to two and a half centimetres. They also heralded the start of the calving season when the birth of thousands of baby animals of all shapes, colours and persuasions would begin to rejuvenate the wild.

It was during this recuperative period that Paul initiated a five-day vehicle game count, its main purpose being to spotlight areas where game congregated and, as such, would be possible hunting grounds for predators. Where impalas associate together in large groups one usually finds cheetahs close by; and where zebras,

With the first rains of the season, tracks around Tuli were awash within hours. In conditions such as this, a landrover could get bogged up to its axle.

wildebeest, buffaloes or any of the larger antelopes predominate, lions are never far away. Each vehicle endeavoured to record the number and type of game spotted on any given journey, which would be to a pre-determined look-out or location ear-marked for that day as a search area.

The count certainly showed this flowering, unsung corner of eastern Botswana to be rich in a wide variety of wildlife. There was an estimated three hundred head of elephant in the area, while in one splendid herd of eland—animals one would be lucky to surprise on foot—we counted more than once, from look-outs, up to a hundred head. The ostrich population was not high, but secretary birds, and kori bustards, the world's heaviest flying birds, always figured well in counts. Smaller varieties of antelope like steenbok, klipspringer and duiker all appeared to thrive in reasonable numbers. Likewise, smaller Felidae such as serval, wild cat, caracal and the delightfully named black-footed cat. Bat-eared foxes and black-backed jackals were plentiful along with a healthy

93

smattering of nocturnal "cats" that shared the night's plunder with the foxes and the jackals. Among than were the pretty, small-spotted genet, an avid tree-climber, and the bigger African civet, sometimes erroneously called the "civet cat". In fact, both civet and genet belong in the order Carnivora and are classified within the same Family as the mongoose.

Shortly after the big curtain-raiser to the wet that nearly over-whelmed us we encountered our first Tuli lion. We were heading back to camp at the time, hastened on by midday's relentless approach. Suddenly snapping a half-shaft, "Lulu" became bogged down at the soggy perimeter of a wide vlei. "Lulu" had a winch attachment but that did not help us. There was not a single tree or like object near us around which we could wrap the winch cable so as to hoist the vehicle out, neither did we have the means of call-ing up the other Landrover to tow us out. The one thing in our favour was the time of day. It meant the other Landrover was possibly back at camp, or at least on its way there. The question of the moment was who was to trek the 14 or so kilometres back through the bush to get it? I didn't rush to volunteer. Paul and Gulubane, on the other hand, didn't seem to mind either way. Eventually Gulubane said that he should go as no one knew the topography of the area better than he.

Carpeted in silky, knee-length grass the colour of under-ripe wheat, the vlei was a vast amphitheatre about 200 metres in diameter, encircled by attentive stands of tall mopane with low scrub crowded in between. Towards the centre, like a lone figure on a characterless stage, stood a solitary tree, slender and erect, with well-dressed boughs of leafy green that looked like they might provide a welcome shade from the noonday sun. As it looked as though we were in for a long wait Paul and I settled ourselves under this tree. Soon we had a small fire licking away and brewed some tea.

A recce of the vlei and its immediate environs had revealed a well-trodden game trail leading up over some sandy hillocks and down to a narrow waterway that though in vigorous flow, looked as if it might be fordable. This could be a way out for the vehicles, we

94

An overnight bivouac en route to Tuli from Palapye.

thought. Apart from this, there was little else to excite our interest. Certainly there was no game to speak of, most of it having gone to ground with the approach of noon. We did likewise. It was while we were sitting under the green umbrella of this tree in perfect peace that we heard a throbbing rumble, a sound that cut the still repose of thought like thunder. At the instant Paul whispered ''lion'' I stiffened instinctively. Moments later it emerged, as if invoked, from out of a stand of mopane straight across from us. Stopping motionless... it stared in our direction. It is as well to remember at moments like this, that if a charging lion can knock down a ton buffalo and kill it with a single, savage bite, then a frail human must be like taking on a jelly-baby. Moreover, whether you think it's within biting distance or not, becomes irrelevant when you also remember that a charging lion has been known to cover a distance of 100 metres in little over three seconds! Sensing this jelly-baby's unease, Paul reassured me. ''It's alright'', he said, ''he looks like he's just giving us the once-over''. Indeed, we must have presented a curious sight propped up in the middle of nowhere with our cups of tea and deck-chairs, as much a part of

the regular scene as chimps holding a tea party in the centre of Pic-
cadilly Circus!

Taking a good look at him through my binoculars, a magnificent
strawberry-maned fellow in the peak of condition, it was easy to
appreciate how it is that the lion has come to be dubbed the king
of the jungle. In the untamed bush that is its rightful domain, the
spectacle of a strapping male lion with such a fine head and mane
as this one produces a sensation difficult to convey to the mundane
world beyond. Soon he tired of observing us and, turning nonchalantly, lurched off into the mass of mopane behind him, as
nimbly as he'd arrived. Gulubane eventually got back in the other
Landrover and it wasn't long before we'd pulled ''Lulu'' from the
bog, made our way round the vlei and across the river with few hit-
ches save the inconvenience of water leaking in through minor
cracks and under the doors. Once free, we learned that his day
hadn't been entirely free of the odd frisson either, such as ''playing
tag'' with an obstreperous lioness. For nearly a third of his journey
back to camp, it seems she had dogged his footsteps to within but
a few paces. Happily for him the uncomfortable liaison was never
consummated.

Paul and Lena Bottriell with Sir Archibald James' King Cheetah and common cheetah skins. Thakeham, Surrey.

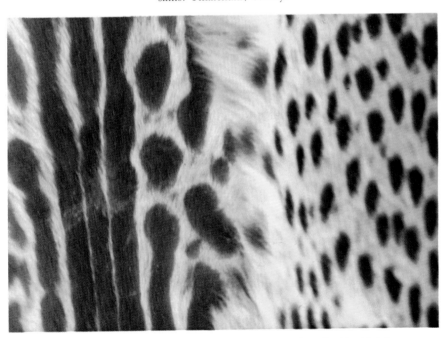

Comparison of a King Cheetah skin (left) and cheetah skin (right).

King Cheetah. This photograph was taken in 1975 (Kruger Park, South Africa).

Adolescent common cheetah and King Cheetahs at the De Wildt Cheetah Breeding Station, South Africa.

Between Two Worlds

As the November days came and went, news of the King Cheetah didn't. It was a job at times keeping the child within from feeling sad. In such moments there is a danger of latching onto colourful, if not sensational, snippets of information that end up going nowhere. Latching onto objectivity comes harder. There was the time, for instance, when the "bush telegraph" brought word of "three King Cheetahs—shot and killed" the week previously over the border. It was the sort of news for which one could well be forgiven a lapse of objectivity!

At once we made for a place called Alldays some eighty kilometres away in South Africa, a place quaintly so-named by early settlers because game were reputed to pass by in their thousands, on their way to drink, "all the days". When we got there, the shooting of three big cats was hot news. We were in the bushveld of the northernmost corner of the Transvaal—open, rambling bush country made cheerless by the taming effect of ranching (the gleaming spires of silver and gold modernity still being some way further south). Indeed, it was on a farm in this very area that a King Cheetah was shot and its skin collected, back in the 1940s. To date in our research this is the only King Cheetah known officially to hail from South Africa. The story this time round was that a farmer on the outskirts of Alldays—in reality, a tiny one-horse town boasting little more than a friendly roadside store and cafe, and "cottage hospital"—had been carrying out a random check of his property when he came across three large cats running through one of the empty paddocks. Automatically he took aim with his rifle—as is the way with so many farmers in this part of the world—and pot-shotted them, apparently killing all three: the practised aim of the trigger-happy shot. We'd already run the gamut of emotions since first receiving the news in Tuli; between then and arrival at Alldays we had calmed down. The man spoke to us in snatches of broken English and Afrikaans. He told us: "Ag, I had to shoot it, you understand—the blixen was donnering my calves!" There had been two cats, not three, and only one, it seems, had been a King Cheetah. It was the usual tale of a farmer shooting first and asking questions later.

Paul asked him what he had done with the carcass after he had skinned it. "Ag, I didn't skin it man", he said, "I've sent it, and the other, intact, down to a taxidermist in Pietersburg whose going to do a lekker job mounting them into a ... how you say... diorama! Like in the museums, y'know?". Well, we certainly hadn't expected this; sending the cat off, carcass and all. In the hands of a good taxidermist this ensured a more authentic mount. It also meant something else of importance to us: a King Cheetah for analysis; skin, skull, skeleton, and if the body hadn't deteriorated too much, some blood, even an examination of the stomach as an indicator of eating habits. Bemoaning the death of a King Cheetah virtually under our noses was one thing; making the most of an unfortunate occurrence was another. Knowing the taxidermist in question, we were certain he'd be able to verify the receipt of a King Cheetah, rather than something else. So we went to see him.

To most South Africans, a nation of heavy smokers at the time, the term "King Cheetah" may be compared with the term "king-size cigarettes" (or, as one gent with a gleam in his eye suggested to me, "king-size beds") and, as such, is no more to them than a descriptive allusion to a king-sized spotted cheetah! And this is exactly what the "Alldays" specimen turned out to be—a very large, ordinary cheetah.

If nothing else this story illustrates something of the sorry plight of cheetahs in an area where they were officially classified as vermin. Many farmers simply see cheetahs and similar cats as threats to their livelihood. For some folk, one way around the problem in an age when we are endeavouring to bolster the wild cheetah population, not reduce it, is to encourage farmers to capture them, rather than to kill them. But many just see this as a big hassle; it's easier

98

Site of reported King Cheetah sighting, Tuli.

to shoot them! Our spirits needed lifting after the "Alldays" fiasco and so we returned to Tuli.

In this otherworldly corner of Botswana the only concession to "civilisation" as we know it is a small, discreet and beautifully appointed Lodge tucked away in an arm of the Limpopo. It is open for only a limited period of the year and takes a small number of guests who have to be flown in by Cessna aircraft due to the nature of the terrain. That evening we paid it a rare visit. We had a suprise when we reached it. A truckload of black Batswana suddenly appeared out of the night looking for the "King Cheetah baas and his lady". At first sight the whole incident was rather unnerving, especially given our relative seclusion in Tuli. In the dim glare of torch-light, they all looked wild-eyed, shuffling about uneasily while refusing to talk to anyone but us. For one mad, fleeting moment, considering the sensitivity of the area because of the war in the north, I wondered if we'd suddenly been listed "undesirable aliens", and were about to be escorted from the country! But Gulubane knew they were merely government game

99

scouts from the south. Moreover, they had come to tell us they had all just seen a King Cheetah only a few kilometres from our camp! Caught in their headlights, it had stood momentarily frozen, dazzled by the glare. ''It was like no living animal we had ever seen before in the bush'', their spokesman told us excitedly. Those sitting in the cab of the truck had judged it to be rather larger in size than an impala. When eventually it broke away from the light and scooted down the side of the vehicle, those sitting in front and others standing in the back got a clear view of it and were immediately reminded of the photographs of skins published soon after our arrival. What struck those closest so vividly—and this is significant—were the wide, dark, stripes running the full length of its spine and the lustrous, almost luminous quality of its stark black-and-white coat patterning. Any suggestions of it being a serval were rejected out of hand. There had always been conjecture about whether many of the so-called sightings of King Cheetah were really of serval. But the latter cat is considerably smaller, nearly half the size of King Cheetah in fact, and still looks small in comparison even at night when many animals appear deceptively larger; the play of light from headlamps and shooting-lamps against the black of night gives a false illusion of distance. Compared with the heavy pattern on the King Cheetah pelage, the serval is daintily stippled with just the merest wisps of stripes on the near-frontal dorsal area where spots have joined. Moreover, the serval has distinctively large erect ears that are almost its trademark, they so dominate its appearance.

Thus it seemed hardly credible that a group of between eight and nine professional game scouts, some senior to Gulubane, could have been mistaken! It had puzzled me, I must say, why originally they would only talk to Paul and me about their experience. They did not talk even to Mary, Mike or Steve who had been at the camp the first time they had gone there looking for us. Then I remembered Joseph—and that answered it to some extent. Doubtless even professional game scouts aren't immune to the same feelings of apprehension about not being believed. Little wonder, when you hear comments to the effect that many can't

First King Cheetah cub born in captivity. Photographed at the De Wildt Cheetah breeding sanctuary, 1981.

even tell the difference between a leopard or a cheetah when they see one!

At sunrise the next morning we headed for the scene of the incident. The night before, the scouts had marked out the spot by rolling a large boulder into position. Now, in the awakening light of early morning, and working from the boulder, we scoured the area for fresh pug-marks and other signs, compassing in a wide arc for well on two hours. But little of significance was revealed save for some well-incised spoor, so clear that they looked as though they could have been cast in plaster, of a cheetah that doubtless had been through the area soon after the rains when the earth was still soft and yielding under foot. Now, unfortunately, the earth was like rock. Even the clean, heavy tread of a Landrover would be difficult to distinguish. Already the land was getting thirsty and tracking generally would become more and more difficult as time passed. Indeed, roughly eight hours had elapsed since the sighting of the night before and in that time an animal, especially one that has been startled, can cover a great deal of ground, not stopping until it feels relatively secure.

The only thing left to do, with the scouts still adamant they had seen a King cheetah, was to stake out a dead antelope in the hope it might draw the animal out into the open if it was still around. In setting up the bait it was important that it should be accomplished with as little fuss as possible. It is surprising for example, just how quickly the presence of a camp in an area becomes known to the animals thereabouts; they are careful to avoid it until they no longer feel threatened by it. Finally, a prominent tree offering good cover and an excellent view of the bait area was turned into a hide for an around-the-clock watch.

It has always been a moot point whether or not cheetahs, alone among the big cats, will go to bait. Certainly experiments over the years have shown that they do. However, it was the little known King cheetah we were dealing with, a cat bigger than the ordinary cheetah, whose habits for all we knew could have been more comparable to those of one of the other big cats, the leopard being an obvious choice. One later-discovered fact firmly put paid to any misgivings on this score: a King Cheetah actually shot over a lion-bait! Hence the question of our animal coming or not coming to bait remained debatable at this stage. Nothing happened either that day and night, or any of the following days. Meanwhile, time was directing our sights elsewhere—namely the tentative appointment we'd arranged for early December with Rhodesian Military Command, Salisbury.

Our choice of the Tuli corner as a rendezvous for a search had, in fact, been the cause of some concern among friends and sponsors alike back in England. They agonised over notions of north-eastern Botswana being in some way similar to Flanders in the First World War. Admittedly, their concern wasn't entirely unwarranted. One could still remember the fatal shooting, prior to our arrival, of two white Rangers and an Eton school-boy by a Botswana Defence Forces patrol at a place not more than six kilometres from where we had camped on the Limpopo. The incident was a mindless mistake which greatly embarrassed the government of the country, terrorist movements on the borders with Zimbabwe being often quoted as an influential factor. By the time we'd arrived in Tuli guerilla activity along the border had increased. The relative remoteness of the whole area either side of the Circle meant that it became an attractive haven for terrorists (or terrs as we christened them) from time to time.

As for the BDF, none of their patrols ever gave us any cause for alarm; indeed, we never encountered any. Not so the Lodge where, on one occasion, a squad of BDF "invaded" the place and proceeded, for well over an hour, to brandish loaded FN rifles, their safety catches off, under the noses of a group of terrified guests. This was not the sort of activity calculated to bring them rushing back! Such are the forgotten effects of wars in Africa; effects that include the drastic reduction of wildlife (what with the bombing raids, the mines and the wholesale poaching that goes on, usually on the part of some government-invited foreign presence, as in Angola) and disrupts the tourist trade that is now very much the life-blood of so many countries on the African continent.

As a result of the Rhodesian war the number of foreign tourists to game parks and lodges around southern Africa, as a whole, had dropped dramatically, with some establishments being forced to close as a result. But though incidents like the one that happened at the Lodge may have passed us by, others of a similarly frightening nature didn't. We were working a thick area of bush between the Shashe and the Circle. It was just a few days prior to our taking off for Rhodesia (Gulubane and an enthusiastic team remaining behind to hold the fort). Most of the morning had been spent patrolling on foot, stopping at vantage points to survey the immediate surroundings. Living in the bush for long spells, one's eyesight and reflexes sharpen up remarkably. Nevertheless, it is an inconvenient fact of life in bush work that the concentration required by observation, especially in areas of dense cover, can be very taxing. Not surprisingly, it is at such times that one is most likely to make a mistake. Certainly Paul's spotting ability is particularly acute because he spent so much time in the bush as a boy. Even so, given his unpredictability, I wasn't quite sure what to expect when, suddenly and unceremoniously, he shoved me head-first into some tangled bush without a moment's notice! Only too soon his reason became apparent.

Peering through a dappled shield of vegetation as best I could, given my situation, I could just make out, a mere fifty metres from us and heading in our direction, a ragged line of Africans fording the Shashe where it appeared shallowest. Crouched low on the ground, I stared hard between the boughs and fronds impeding my view down to the river. At first they all seemed to be carrying stout sticks. Then I noted with a shiver, as they came purposefully closer, that they were carrying a lethal array of firearms. I didn't move, or make a sound. Must be terrs, I thought to myself, beating a hasty retreat from over the border, perhaps even heading into an ambush. It is amazing just what can move about in secluded bush unnoticed. It was not improbable that an advance force of Rhodesian militia, pre-empting their route, had already crossed over. Such things were possible. During the later stages of the war Rhodesian forces frequently made incursions into Botswana nearly all along the border between the two countries. One big push, complete with air support, that occurred while our expedition was still based on the Limpopo, took them all the way into Francistown, 100 kilometres into the country, on some pro-fessed ''clean-up'' operation and straight out again.

The men crept nearer and nearer, like a band of haunted mice. Birds and insects ceased their prattle. Indeed, the whole bush seemed to be marking their progress as breathlessly and expec-tantly as I was. Even the tenacious little weaver birds in the bran-ches overhead had left off building their nests and had spirited themselves away.

As we were by the river the ground was covered by a dank layer of rotting leaves that dulled the sound of footfalls. Thus, hunched forward, weapons frozen at the ready, the men edged intently and noiselessly along the sheltered bank towards where we were crouching, well-hidden by the screen of thick, lush bush. Closer and closer they came. A signal from Paul meant ''flick back the safety''. Time moved into slow-motion as over cold barrels of steel,

Bush track between Pitsane and Limpopo, Northern Tuli — Paul Bottriell and Game Scout Gulubane.

with the blood thundering in my ears, eyes narrowed, I marked their every step. One glimpse of us in those bushes, armed and dressed in khaki bush gear, and few questions would be asked before the guns would open fire. The war Paul and I had so casually stumbled into declared no boundaries; with the heart-rending finality we were soon to learn a second time round, all were ripe for the slaughter whatever their colour or political doctrine.

The men passed by and vanished out of our sight. We remained where we were for a good hour, waiting and watching as we had done so often before, though never in such cheerless circumstances. We neither saw nor heard the terrs again, which was probably just as well, for soon afterwards, a Rhodesian helicopter gunship, followed by another minutes later, flew overhead on a quick sortie up the Shashe then back into Rhodesia. Gulubane always declined to accompany us when we ventured this far up: "Oh, nooo!", he'd exclaim, slapping the side of his face in a gesture of comic despair. "One look... one look at this black face

105

in those bushes," he would say, "and I'm gone... like—dead!".
Hearing this the first time I couldn't help smiling to myself and
thinking how melodramatic Gulubane could be when he wanted
to. Now, with this particular experience amongst my souvenirs, he
and I could have made a good double-act! We spoke of the incident
to no one, not even Gulubane. What with our impending trip to
Salisbury, it was the surest way to invite misunderstanding.

The Geese fly North

We took it in turns to drive through to Beitbridge, the tiny border control town that then marked the southern gateway to Rhodesia. The route there, through dry uninspiring bush, was itself dirt-dry and uncompromising. Clouds of fine dust belched into the Landrover from every angle as though it was a colander leaving us looking like plaster-of-Paris figures. Arriving at the "Bridge" any discomfort we were feeling quickly became secondary to the unmistakeable mood of menace hanging over all. It made our skins tingle under the pall of dust—and we hadn't even crossed the border into Rhodesia yet. Indeed, it seemed almost stagey, on this side of the river at least. Certainly the folk at South African customs appeared to be fighting some minor war of their own as they went about their duties with an air of suffering that could only have been practised!

Not until we began to cross the narrow-spanned bridge over the Limpopo that linked the two quite disparate countries did the theatrical suddenly become powerfully real. For such a tiny, one-street town, the place was bustling; only the solitary sentries on that long, slender bridge remained motionless. Military vehicles were everywhere; and everyone, soldier or civilian, man or woman, was armed. It was from here that convoys of civilian vehicles escorted by military "gunships" plied their way several times daily back and forth into the heart of the country. They went westwards to Bulawayo, historic Matabele capital, its name taken from that of the Zulu King Chaka's kraal, or northwards to Fort Victoria, Gwelo and, finally, to Salisbury, 600 kilometres away, our ultimate destination.

With the escalation of the war this became the safest way to get about, though "safety" as such could hardly be guaranteed when even stretches of innocent-looking bitumen were likely to be studded with landmines hidden and re-sealed just under the sur-

107

face of the tar. Even in their cars people remained armed. What struck you most about it all was that weapons weren't worn with an ostentatious swagger, like bold Hollywood badges of courage. The cool, elegant 30-year-old from the suburbs, small children and large dog ensconced in the station-wagon, her hefty 9 mm sitting snug in it's holder slung round her slender hips, attested to that. Interestingly enough, no reference to our ever having passed through Rhodesian border control at Beitbridge appeared in our passports, an incongruity difficult to explain under the circumstances.

We drove on through the town, a still atmosphere of foreboding hanging over us. We had cleared customs and passport control where, despite the war, an open and cheerful air of resolve made a refreshing change from the gruff officiousness on the other side. By contrast, the town itself seemed withdrawn and abstracted, as if repelled by what man-made pain lay beyond its bounds. Just a few kilometres out, we were halted at a roadblock by a black para in combat gear. Half a dozen others, black and white, ambled about in an easy, unhurried way, their automatics slung over a shoulder or looped under an arm. It seems we had just missed the last convoy and would be foolish to go alone.

Not having experienced war at first-hand before but only the vibrations of it, a distant bell suddenly began to ring in my head. "Foolish to tackle the way alone"; the words came at me like an intro to some dream sequence not of my own making and the wonder of it was dulling my perception of things. There was a face at the window and its mouth was moving, but I seemed unable to respond as if thought and reflex had become suddenly immobilised. Paul appeared to be just about as vacant and tongue-tied as. A white officer strolled over. "Good afternoon", he drawled cheerily, a warm smile lighting up raunchy, weather-blown features. Glancing at the legend painted along the side of the Landrover, he leaned an arm casually on the window frame and peered at us quizzically. "Going through to Salisbury?" "Yes!", we nodded vigorously. "I seeee", he said, mysteriously, rubbing his chin. "It's a long trip you know... especially this late in the

The author, game-viewing in the Tuli-region of north-east Botswana.

day. And besides...'', he chortled, giving the Landrover a hearty whack with the palm of his hand, ''these things aren't exactly the world's fastest machines!'' Suddenly I could speak: ''Er... I take it you don't think we should go through to Salisbury, er... today!''. ''Well—I can't exactly stop you'', came the cautious reply. ''By the same token, you'd really be better advised to wait till morning. There's a convoy leaving here at seven am, and another at eleven. You see, late afternoon is one of the worst times to travel. Some attempt it on their own. Others aren't so lucky—only yesterday, at just about this time, not twelve kilometres from here along this Fort Victoria/Salisbury road'', he pointed to the turning up ahead, ''a local farmer driving back to his farm was ambushed and killed''.

Little more needed to be said. We headed back towards Beitbridge. Not long afterwards, in the relative sanctuary of the beer garden in the town's tiny, colonial-style hotel, pivot of Beitbridge's social life, we were given further cause to wonder about the state of things to come. That evening as we sipped welcome draughts of iced Castle Pilsner and looked out over the little town's north/south approaches, all was quiet and still. Nowhere was any tangible destruction or desolation obvious to the eye. Yet it was there alright, there, behind the joviality, the pained esprit, the friendly hand extended to a stranger; there, in the eyes of the men, and the few women, lounging, drinking, sometimes laughing around us; there, in steel, strapped to their hips.

The local vegetation was reminiscent of Tuli, with the road north out of Beitbridge winding through a lonely stretch of bush beaded with heavily wooded granite outcrops and jagged lines of kopjes that made it a paradise for leopards and guerillas alike. Indeed, it offered the toughest type of terrain to counter terrorist attacks, the lofty, well-foliaged peaks stretched between vast tracts of uninhabited bush affording excellent views of the roads for miles around and providing ideal cover for a surprise attack. There was no question of camping out on our stopover at Beitbridge and after a restless, dream-filled night's sleep at the hotel in simple surroundings that answered basic needs, we joined the early morning convoy at the roadblock assembly point, just outside the town where we'd been stopped the previous day. A fleet of private cars, comprising some twenty vehicles or more, eventually made up the convoy, with a goodly number of passengers distributed between them.

Every convoy, whatever its ultimate destination, was accompanied by several armed vehicles, or gunships. Generally the number attached to any one convoy depended on how many civilian cars there were. The so-called gunship was by no means a sophisticated vehicle but simply a mine-proofed, half-ton pick-up, economical on fuel, and nifty about the roads, with a rotating gun emplacement perched in the open back manned by a gunner—looking like a man and his bren gun seated in a 44-gallon drum that swivelled from side to side—while a couple of others, not including the driver rode shotgun.

We ourselves collected a passenger extra when a young off-duty soldier hitched a ride with us to Salisbury. Returning from leave, he was a quiet, unassuming character both in person and physique who, as a schoolboy, had left Scotland with his parents to settle in South Africa. On a subsequent holiday to Rhodesia he "fell in love with the country", so much so, that he joined the Security Forces later as a volunteer, to fight in the war! He was fighting a questionable war in which, as some would see it, he had no direct emotional or blood tie, no "right" to be involved, as it were. There were dozens of others like Scotty around at that unfortunate time, from Canada and America, Australia and New Zealand, catchers all in the same shadow.

Shortly after taking off on the first leg of the journey to Fort Vic via Bubye River—pronounced "booby"—we were coasting along at a good 120 kph when, without warning we began to lose speed drastically. Within minutes we'd dropped back from near the head of the convoy until there wasn't a single car behind us. Finally, we stopped altogether. Vehicles were expected to travel fast in convoy and at a steady speed; they were not supposed to stop under any circumstances unless authorised to do so. We had stopped because we had acquired a puncture. A puncture! We had driven our Landrovers through open bush, over thorn scrub and rock, through rivers and along pock-marked, weather-bitten hillsides and never had a puncture between them. Now, at the least convenient moment imaginable, on the first decent bit of tarred road we'd driven over in months, it had happened!

According to the convoy commander about 600 terrs were known to have been concentrated along this particular stretch of road very recently. Remembering this I thought my heart would burst from my body as Paul and Scotty moved swiftly to change the offending nearside front tyre and I guarded the rear, my ·308 at the ready, loaded and primed, the instruction "shoot anything that moves" repeating in my head like some cruel chant.

It took less than three minutes to change the tyre, which just goes to show how much a sense of timelessness takes over in situations such as this, as if one were sleep-walking fully awake. One's senses register every sight, sound or smell, in microscopic detail. I recall no bird song—a sure barometer of tension—nor any wind; I

The Bubye River Patrol, Rhodesia.

remember only the pounding of my heart and the frantic industry of men about some urgent business. I can't say how long I'd been standing there when the gunship and crew appeared, like a band of avenging angels, from out of nowhere and glided to a halt beside us.

By this time the convoy was now a good way ahead of us and our only hope of catching it up looked to be at the lonely roadside halt of Bubye River some fifty kilometres on, the first scheduled rest and refuelling point after Beitbridge. An attractive thatched, bush-style hotel was really all that marked the spot. There was a chance the convoy would wait for us there... five, ten minutes extra perhaps, but not much longer. Fortunately, we had brought the faster Landrover up from Tuli, a choice that was no accident. We didn't, however, reckon on yet another hair-raising encounter delaying us.

We were on our own again, a chill solitary feeling that unnerved the senses. Paul was driving and I was seated in the middle between him and Scotty. Our passenger carried an army-issue automatic pistol, handy at point-blank range as it enables one to fire a barrage of shots without re-loading. A dark blur appeared on the road ahead of us; it quivered unsteadily in the growing heat and Paul and Scotty stiffened in their seats. Suddenly a hand came up behind me, pushing me down onto the floor. As Paul slammed the accelerator flat, I watched, mesmerised, as the bolt of the automatic was rammed into place. An ambush, I thought! Mines buried under the bitumen surface was one thing; being ambushed was quite another—even more real and potentially more bloody. Minutes passed... and we were still intact, no fiery brand rending us asunder. We were lucky. Others weren't always so. The blur assumed the shape of a donkey cart and passed harmlessly out of sight.

As none of this was doing my constitution any good Bubye was a welcome sight, especially as the convoy was still there. The place was alive with vehicles and uniforms. The bar, a diverting mud and thatch affair waggishly named "The Bubye Trap", was doing well. The hotel had been closed for some time to houseguests, having been appropriated by the military. As far as ground forces were concerned, this comprised three groups of both black and white troops: The Rhodesian Light Infantry, or RLI, the Territorials, and the "Volunteer Force".

After a short, gratifying respite here, we reassembled in convoy and drove on. The sense of renewed well-being was short-lived as some kilometres out, we came to an African village that had been attacked in the early hours of the morning. The village store had

113

been ransacked; the villagers' huts had been plundered and rased to the ground; and perhaps hardest to understand, their cattle had been killed. Government militiamen were already on the scene and the convoy was urged not to linger. Smoke still hung, ghostly and ominous, round the debris, while the carcasses of cattle by the roadside were already bloated and fly-blown.

The village nestled in a fertile undulation, almost a valley, in the shadow of a line of kopjes garlanded with greenery and granite boulders that clung to its flanks like warts. With plenty of running water near at hand, the tiny habitation consisted of a dozen or more neat pole and daga (mud and thatch) huts, each with its own vegetable garden that provided for most of it's owner's basic needs. Now, however, all was in ruin; now there stood only the gutted, charred remains of what were once the humble shelters of humble folk whose only ''crime'' was that they had little need of or regard for the political principle of whoever ruled in Salisbury then, Harare now.

Already the place stank of decaying cattle flesh. Here and there one saw aimless figures trying to salvage some meat or what was left of a motley pocket of possessions. Paul was quick to remind me that to the simple rural African, his cattle is his pension. Thus such a loss without compensation is a devastating blow. Down by the river crouched two old women gently rocking to and fro, wailing their woes to the skies; there was no easing their despair with fashionable rhetoric ringing chords of nationalist fervour.

Oddly enough, just outside the village, on passing out of a narrow gully that couldn't have been more than ten metres across, the entire convoy was brought to a standstill. Where the route wound over a concrete conduit, the road had completely caved in leaving a real snake's pit of a hole filled with jagged chunks of rubble that no saloon car could possibly get over. To anyone with half a brain, it didn't look like one of Mother Nature's little accidents! The area was a notorious blind-spot. The substantial size of our convoy kept us relatively safe from attack; a few cars would have provided ripe pickings.

Three quarters of an hour and a makeshift bridge later, the prob-

114

lem of the convoy becoming mobile again was happily resolved. Later still, when the turning to Zimbabwe ruins loomed up, it seemed to me, in this land obsessed by the age-old "what's ours we hold" ethos, a stunning reminder of how today's victories are tomorrow's dust. This "proud Kingdom of Monomotapa", as chronicled by the sixteenth-century Portuguese, was a city-state apparently unique south of Egypt, the ruins dating back to before 300 AD, possibly the product of some ancient Bantu civilisation. A little way from here, 290 kilometres on from Beitbridge, the convoy pulled into Fort Victoria. A pioneer town with a flavour all it's own, Fort Victoria has been as strategically important in the contemporary history of Rhodesia/Zimbabwe as it was in the early days of settlement. A vital link in the life-giving transport route from Fort Tuli to the north, it was later a powerhouse of strength in the first Matabele war, a time commemorated for years afterwards in the ringing of the curfew bell at the old fort, each evening at nine. Thrust into conflict once again, her citizens, men and women, young and old, ambled about their daily business in between casually stopping to chat in the sun, carrying with the shopping a loaded FN, or pistol, nonchalantly slung over a shoulder or round a waist. It was like another world.

At Umvuma, 101 kilometres north of Fort Victoria, the entire convoy left us. The last leg of the journey to here, thankfully, had been uneventful, but the familiar tension quickly returned as we continued on alone... solitary travellers on a deserted two-hundred-kilometre-long highway through to Salisbury, the capital. I don't believe one of us uttered a syllable until we reached a tiny hiccough of a place called Enkeldoorn, at lunchtime. Like a lonely oasis in a desert of uncertainties, the quaint wayside inn we stopped at for a bite to eat might just as easily have been a cosy, olde worlde country pub set deep in the sylvan groves of peaceful rural England... if it had not been for the melancholy figure of a man with one leg missing, the ubiquitous FN in hand—both like badges of some unexpurgated fate—who sat dreaming over a beer, and for another two figures with limbs in plaster hobbling silently along on crutches. For me, it was the nearest I'd ever come to Limbo, its occupants hardly seeming inclined to speak, let alone look at one another. It was a relief to get to Salisbury and back to the business that had brought us to this half-nirvana world in the first place. Salisbury was a surprise. A capital city with the feel of a bighearted country town, it displayed all of the friendliness we had met elsewhere in the country, with one noticeable difference: the tension beneath the smile bubbled less vigorously. Our first priorities, once we'd settled ourselves, were meetings at the Department of Wildlife, then Military Operations at Command HQ, the initial response from each having been most encouraging when we'd originally broached the question of a possible drop into the Honde. That the meetings should take place in that order was important; without Wildlife's approval there would be no drop, military sanction or no. Having said that, any final decision from Wildlife rested very much on an all-clear from Military Command. Catch-22. The decision, either way, depended as much on the approval of the one as it did of the other!

The result of a warm and enthusiastic meeting with the Chief Wildlife Warden left us in little doubt that the department would give the proposed mission it's full support with all the necessary permits, if and when we got the go-ahead from the military. On this score, it is true to say, there had never been any room for illusions. It seems the war situation had taken a serious downturn in the weeks since we had first approached Army Command. In fact, our chosen area had come to be considered one of the "hottest" zones in the whole Rhodesian theatre... so it was tactfully explained to us by the youthful Colonel assigned to handle our request. Impressive in a laid-back, officer-gentleman manner, there was about him a refreshing modesty, a warmth, that reflected very much the style of his peers.

Our chosen area, one of the most densely vegetated stretches of bush in the country, had been extensively mined and for this reason had fallen under strict martial law, its few scattered villagers having already been moved out to safer ground. Naturally there could be no question of going into such an area without military support of some kind. Here was the rub: with the Security Forces

116

coming under increasing pressure each day as the war continued, military support was no longer available. The Honde exercise was aborted before it had barely begun to kick. Looking back, I'm still amazed they even considered us or our proposal. Perhaps we provided a pleasant diversion.

We didn't return to Botswana straightaway; instead we seized the opportunity in the time left to tidy up some loose ends of research, leads on skins, sightings and the like. There was of course the inevitable share of recent rubble to sift through. One in particular was charming. We were told about a man who was said to have kept a King Cheetah as a pet and had apparently had its remains stuffed and mounted; what's more, it was reputedly still in his possession at his home in Bulawayo! Such a story promised a wealth of detail about the King Cheetah's habits, character traits, etc. Unfortunately, the story was a red herring, even though it came to us direct from the mouth of a well-known white hunter and collector. So much for the African's supposed penchant for gilding the lily. From what we'd experienced to date, their white brethren took a lot of beating!

Our return to Tuli found that all was not well. Besides their being not even a hint of oddly-marked cheetahs, our team, according to Gulubane, had very nearly been arrested by government game scouts. Only the fact that they were a part of the expedition, apparently, had saved them! It seems that, in the absence of Gulubane, they had been "caught" chasing game in the Landrover with a view to getting some sensational photographs. It was difficult to justify, and certainly not complimentary to the expedition. It was the sort of thing that gives expeditions a bad name and destroys the goodwill of a people or a government. Moreover, apart from the obvious strain and complications it can give rise to, it can also make game in calf abort and other game turn rogue, chasing vehicles at the slightest provocation, with the result that some person ends up getting needlessly killed and the unfortunate animal shot!

Maybe Africa brings out the macho in people in more ways than we care to recognise. Certainly, with her genuine dangers and striking capacity to surprise, Africa provides challenges enough without having to import any cheap thrills. A woeful incident we heard about on our trip north is perfectly illustrative. At a small game reserve in the Transvaal, a tour guide—or "game scout" as some are wont to title themselves—was taking a vehicle-load of guests around on safari. Spotting a lusty herd of elephants a short way off, he decided to stop the vehicle, decant himself and clients, and go the distance on foot to get as close as possible. Now one doesn't mess around with elephants at the best of times, small game park or not! In this instance, however, what followed was a tragic litany of mistakes that should never have happened. The guide, for reasons known only to him, wasn't armed—a cardinal sin. There wasn't even a firearm in his vehicle. In addition, the herd included a number of newborn calves, always a situation to be treated with delicacy. And he failed to keep his clients together—the acid test for anyone claiming to have a responsible bush knowledge. The result was that someone, somehow, got between a big cow and her small calf. The cow charged, the guide climbed a tree, and the unfortunate someone got trampled to death.

Fortunately our team's stupid behaviour didn't mar the expedition's reputation to any extent. Nevertheless, it seemed that it might be better for all concerned if Mary, Mike and Steve parted company with the expedition. Little over a week or so later, all three were scheduled to return to their respective homes anyway, leaving Paul, Gulubane and I at Tuli for at least another month to carry on the good work. With the calving season all but upon us, it was going to be difficult not to be distracted by the parade of attractions which were becoming increasingly evident anywhere one cared to look in this unique garden paradise.

118

Limpopo Idyll

After the rains that had nearly overwhelmed us, the bush around the camp remained sparkling with vigour well into the new year, its lush, leafy vegetation dressed in glistening shades of chartreuse and jade and bright emerald green, like the most brilliant impressionist painting. Here and there on branches and bushes overhanging freshly quenched waterholes, the nests of tree-frogs filled with new-laid eggs, dangled like bundles of fluffy white candy-floss. Transcending it all was the scent of the bush and the varied sounds of birdsong.

Traditional prey for cheetah, with the bucks sporting splendid crowns of lyre-shaped horns, impala antelopes abounded in Tuli.

Around the perimeter of the camp lived two to three hundred head of impala. One of the most graceful of the antelopes, it is also known as the "black-heeled" antelope, an original title derived from the tufts of black hair picturesquely adorning its back heels. At home in many kinds of country as long as it is within range of water, the impala is prolific throughout Africa from Botswana northward. I never tired of seeing numbers of these fleet creatures, surely the champion jumpers of Africa, springing across open ground in single leaps that could easily be three metres high and more than twice that in length. They performed elegant arabesques against the sky as they leaped away from the threat of some near-by predator—or merely for the joy of jumping. In the mating season, gleaming rusty-coated bucks, sporting splendid crowns of lyre-shaped horns, run harems of up to fifty ewes each, occasionally more, simultaneously keeping jealous eyes on straying wives and wilful rivals. Many a duel results, sometimes with fatal repercussions for challenger or defender... or both. Needless to say life is a constant adventure, particularly harrowing for the male! At least they can look forward to a little rest and recreation with the coming of the breeding season when the harems transform into well organised nurseries bursting with perfectly behaved, velvety bambies. Indeed, where impalas congregate in large numbers, as near our camp, they seem to form an enormous crèche—absolutely delightful to see! The first time I came face to face with a newborn impala fawn standing all alone under a mopane tree, its huge eyes transfixed by the approach of what must have been the first human it had ever seen (hence its lack of fear) I could have reached out and touched it. I did not do so because its mother, not far away at the time with the herd, might well have abandoned it. A harsh price to pay for one heartfelt touch, perhaps, but then the wild is full of such lessons.

There can be few more perfect moments, when wandering in some untamed setting, than when you gaze upon a baby animal taking its first halting steps. Within just two hours of an impala ewe dropping its young, the daintily-moulded creature can run as fast as its mother. There are other pocket miracles. Standing no more than a foot at the shoulder, warthog piglets, tiny replicas of their parents, comically imitate the adults' characteristic manner of running. We frequently came across a sounder of six or seven of these gregarious and speedy runners. Having got wind of us, or of some other unfamiliar or threatening presence, they would go tearing off in close formation in the opposite direction like little squad cars on patrol, their tufted, rangy tails erected straight and stiff as radio

120

aerials. Then there were newborn elephant calves, a couple of feet at the shoulder at most, standing within minutes of birth and walking within the hour; and zebra foals, as perfect and as pleasing to the eye as any thoroughbred.

Even adult animals took on a richness and a vitality that can only be attributed to the season. The appearance of bat-eared foxes always occasioned much delight. Pretty, greyish-toned animals, smaller than the jackal, they feed predominantly at night, the radar system of their remarkably large disc-shaped ears allowing them to pick up the sounds of lizards, insects and small rodents. Elsewhere around Tuli, stately kudus, considered by some to be the most impressive of all the antelopes, moved in intimate herds in areas abounding in buffalo thorn and acacia where the branches of one or the other were often mistaken for the animal's spiralling horns. And no trail would ever be complete without at least one secretary bird strutting airily about in its elegant, tail-coated ensemble, the long feathers behind its prim, almost disapproving glance, jutting out like a clutch of pens. Shades of Threadneedle Street, indeed! In more ways than one the secretary bird is unique. The kori bustard on the other hand, though an equally prepossessing character, is not; it even has a cousin in Australia with almost identical looks. It is the world's heaviest flying bird, weighing up to 20 kilograms or more. Though generally reputed to behave erratically at the sight of a human, the kories around Tuli were of a curiously unflappable type. The strongest reaction our sudden appearance near one ever solicited was a stately turn of the head, a benign glance, and an unhurried, stately stroll away!

Then there was the cheetah. A difficult animal to spot in the wild at the best of times, particularly when lying prostrate in some straw-coloured grass with just its head erect—a most characteristic pose—many a person looking for one has missed it sitting motionless on its haunches looking straight at him, simply because the cat's general colouring and overall gaunt shape can make it look no different from a dead, jutting tree stump. Often, the merest flick of an ear will be all that gives it away. Little wonder that searching for the hermit King was not child's-play, with every

Trees mowed down by elephants sometimes make ideal 'social trees' for cheetahs. In a quiet corner of the bush, we photographed this adult male cheetah urinating, or marking, the trunk of one such social tree.

stump a potential cheetah, and every cheetah a potential King Cheetah. There was one cheetah I saw, however, that was at least a princess. Having the wind in our favour enabled us to watch her passage from very close up. She looked in the peak of condition, her coat rich, the sylph-like body strong and supple. Striding purposefully through the bush, her cubs arrayed behind her like dutiful attendants, she held her lovely head high, yet remained sharp to every nuance of sound or movement in the vicinity. Never before had I seen a cat in the wild move with as much grace and dignity as she.

In and around the camp animal life thrived abundantly. There was the resident water monitor lizard, for example, which haunted the metres-high riverbank flanking the camp where the greenery was at its most dank and overgrown. The unexpected sight of an enormous specimen of characteristic prehistoric look didn't do my heart-rate any good one still morning when its inches thick, metre-long reptilian tail met my foot for the first time. Till then, I'd always thought I had an affinity with lizards, born as I had been into a land of frilled necks, blue-tongues, goannas, and thorny devils. But that was Australia. In Africa, water monitors can grow to more than two metres in length—and that's a lot of dragon to meet unexpectedly. Though subsisting on a variety of aquatic and riverbank creatures, they are partial to crocodiles' eggs. So too are mongooses; and there were lots of these attractive little characters to be seen around the immediate environs of the camp at any given time.

Mongooses are among Africa's most efficient smaller predators, with a particular penchant for reptiles. While on my way to breakfast one morning, I was stopped in my tracks by the sight of twenty or more mongooses, making their way into camp along a game trail leading up from the river. Unaware of me, as yet, each was fastidiously foraging in amongst the long finger grass flanking the trail while still remaining in line. Every now and then the leading mongoose would stand bolt upright on its hindlegs and peer around imperiously. Once satisfied there was no danger, it would burst into a stream of chatter which was probably the all-clear signal; then it would rejoin its fellows in the all-consuming task of working the area over for food. Curious to discover exactly how they'd react if I revealed myself, seeing they were so engrossed in what they were doing, I clicked my tongue loudly against the roof of my mouth; for a split second, not one mongoose moved. Then, in a tirade of chatter, each one shot up on its back legs and craned its neck in the direction of the sound. But still they couldn't see me for the various obstructions in the way and after a while returned to what they'd been doing, though noticeably more on guard. I clicked my tongue again and was given a repeat performance. Twice more I clicked my tongue, with similar results, the mongooses getting closer and closer to me by the moment. Eventually, not being able to resist the temptation my new-found power had given me, I came out of hiding and walked straight towards them. To a mongoose, they lifted themselves off the ground by about a foot or more, executed a complete about-turn in mid-air, and to a rising cacophony of horrified cries and mongoose exclamations that could still be heard even as the dust of their departure cleared, they streaked away down the game path the way they'd come. Undaunted, they were back the very next morning—via the *other* end of camp!

Not all visitors were greeted with such cheery nonchalance. Where the large canvas canopy formed our kitchen, it overhung the camp's most prestigious ''piece of furniture'', the huge, prostrate branch of the mashatu tree. Fairly near it's junction with the tree, some hessian sacking had been laid across its girth like a shabrack.

The author enjoying a drink in the shade of the camp's
Mashatu tree.

A little while after the season's first torrential downpour Paul moved the hessian aside one day and found a substantial family of scorpions sheltering there. Being unpleasantly large ones of the more poisonous variety he promptly, and patiently, helped them off the premises. All very amicable on the surface of it. During the rainy season, however, scorpions have an unnerving habit of nestling in one's boots, which at 4.30 in the morning, as one is getting ready for the day's business, comes as an unpleasant surprise. The scorpion's sting is painful, sometimes inducing fever or temporary paralysis, but it seldom proves fatal. With smaller victims it's a different story. Holding its prey between two large lobster-like claws, the scorpion flicks its tail back over itself and stings it to death. Ant-lions are equally vindictive and we had many of them sharing board with us, evidenced by the number of tiny depressions and random, pencil-line tracks all around the ground in camp. Hidden just out of sight with only their pincer-like jaws projecting, ant-lions, or rather their larvae, lie in wait at the bottom of neat, conical sand pits no more than a few centimetres deep ready to grab hold of and suck dry any ants which might stumble into the pits. We had few problems with ants! Then there was the shiny, black mud hornet which visited me in the caravan whenever I chose to type in it. At first I wasn't pleased about the interruptions. The insect would no sooner waltz in through an open window, loaded down with mud, than I would exit through another opening, waving my arms and muttering incantations (you can never trust hornets). The hornet meant no harm of course, so long as it could be left to build as many nests as possible for it's young. Unfortunately, we were far from keen to co-habit with a whole family of hornets and as a result would quietly steal a moment to dismantle her efforts when she wasn't looking, until eventually she appeared to get the message and moved elsewhere. She was a happy sort of hornet though, and didn't seem to mind, so I dubbed her the ''Merry Widow''. On a more serious note, the cocoons of hornets and similar insects, constructed in inconvenient places such as in the shaft of a gun-barrel, or on the eyepiece of a spare pair of binoculars, can have dire, even deadly results.

125

The noise created in and around the camp by the endless stream of insects that came and went during the heat of the day made life hell when you needed a little rest after a morning's foot-slogging in the bush. Little wonder that the area was a haunt for chameleons. A creature as charming in its way as the species of gecko that inhabits northern Queensland, it's quite a revelation to come upon one, with its all-round vision of 360° and prehensile tail, "walking" across the top of tall grass, changing colour according to its immediate surroundings as it does so.

The troupe of Chacma baboons that lived across the river from our camp hadn't been near us since the incident with the leopard. But we had been visited by garrulous vervet monkeys, drawn our way in ever-increasing numbers by the bountiful mashatu that spread its splendour over the camp. They couldn't resist its fruit. Most mornings would find dozens of them festooning the branches, gurgling their delight as they gorged themselves on the precious store. Sometimes these orgies could last for hours... if not interrupted by a little light drama! Early one morning after a late night patrol, an ominous "rat-tat-tat" began to penetrate my sleep. Sounding fearfully like gunfire through the hazy veil of that half-dream, half-awake state, the notion that we were being attacked by some marauding force was enough to wake me up with a violent start. Paul was already awake, and gone; but I didn't have far to look to find him. The great tree overhanging the camp was alive... alive with sixty, eighty or more bloated, gormandising vervets! The frenetic activity on the boughs and branches had brought showers of the tree's shiny-shelled berries down into the camp, rat-tat-tatting onto every surface that could make a noise, from Landrovers to cooking pots, with as many pips and husks adding to the bombardment.

Superimposed on this scene was an irate, rudely-awaken Paul, as God intended him, in full charge shouting at the tree... arms and fists madly flailing the air. Understandably put out by the sight of this raging, six-foot-three naked ape coming straight for them, the tree erupted in a shower of monkeys. With piercing, scolding screams, the monkeys threw themselves into the air from every

126

branch, tumbled down the bank in droves, and streamed away, their indignant hysteria gradually being replaced by the returning quiet of morning. I remember thinking at the time that, after such a curtain-raiser, the rest of the day was bound to seem tame. The monkeys were soon back, however, their love of fruit taking precedence over their fear.

Further away from camp, among the gnarled traces and secretive crevices of the kopje frequented by that wily leopard neighbour of ours there lived in apparent permanent residence a close-knit colony of rock rabbits (known as rock dassies in southern Africa),

Kitchen at Mashatu camp. Prostrate Mashatu tree branch (best 'kitchen furniture') in the foreground, 8ft. ant-hill behind.

engaging creatures which we saw whenever we passed by their rocky fortress. They always kept their distance although we in no way offered the same threat to their continued existence as did the spotted grimalkin who shared the kopje with them. This cat played a kind of bush-style russian roulette with his gregarious neighbours... and rarely missed a shot. While a group of hyrax lay snoozing and sunning itself along the terraced crest of the kopje, the leopard would creep up stealthily behind it, careful not to let the ever-present look-out get wind of him. On getting close enough he would let forth a blood-curdling snarl calculated to put the rabbits into a frenzy. It worked like a charm every time. Some of the rabbits would cast themselves off into what looked to be the nearest, safest direction, down holes or behind boulders. The unlucky ones, in a paroxysm of fear, would lose their footing and plummett down to the ground below.

For some time since returning from the north we had clocked up a considerable number of night searches, starting around midnight and working the bush till first light, then returning to camp for a hearty breakfast of mealie porridge and eggs, or perhaps a delicious warthog steak. This way we naturally doubled our chances of finding a King Cheetah. With the advance of the wet season the heat had intensified; also it had been getting hotter much earlier. Understandably this reduced the length of time at one stretch that we could work in the open comfortably. We had specifically chosen this period of the year for our fieldwork for one simple reason: the calving season is when predators are most active. Moreover, with cheetahs in this part of Africa appearing to drop their own young around the same time, preying on newly born ungulates would obviously be advantageous for any female cheetah with cubs to feed, King or otherwise. Night, therefore, offered an especial degree of danger to game, with more and more predators, not just the purely nocturnal ones, taking advantage of the cooler cover of dark. Consequently, a shooting-lamp was essential to allow one to floodlight the open bush ahead at a given moment. Stalking among the herds of zebra, impala and wildebeest, among others, we would thus frequently pick out the furtive form of a lion, a hyena, a serval, or a caracal—that beautiful cat with the striking tufted ears, otherwise known as the African lynx, which is a lone nocturnal hunter with an impressive talent for catching flying birds.

A dramatic sight common between sunset and dawn was that of a black-backed jackal flitting past like a silvery ghost in pursuit of

128

spring-hares whose eyes would glow like hot coals in the dark. Living in burrows much of the day, and subsisting mainly on roots and bulbs, these queer-looking little hares resembled, at a quick glance, tiny kangaroos, or wallabies, with their long tails helping to propel them across the ground by long leaps and bounds. They seemed a particular favourite of the jackal, a canny creature as legendary in African folklore as the fox is in European. Evident, too, was the spotted and striped brigade. Sometimes we'd be lucky and glimpse a secretive masked civet, snuffling stealthily away into the bush like a cat-burglar. Maybe we'd see a sylph-like genet high up in a tree chasing a reptile or scurrying away from the glare of our lamp to take refuge behind a shrub. Or we'd catch a fleeting glimpse of a dainty black-footed cat as it danced its way out of our light with the poise of a pierrot. There was absolutely no mistaking any of these for a King Cheetah, as has frequently been suggested. Certainly the spotted, arboreal genet with its tiny head, wide-eyed lemur-like expression and long tail, is more reminiscent of an opossum than any large cat. And one could recognise that night prowler of repute, the serval, with its generous outsize ears, almost on sight, even though it can appear deceptively bigger than its lissome self at night because of its long-legged gait. But then, so can lion, or hyena. Certainly, a more broken up, strong black-on-white patterning, such as that of the King Cheetah, the giraffe etc., will stand out better at night. Animals with more regular or so-called ''lighter'' markings, such as the zebra or no markings at all, such as the lion, can actually appear paler at night. A more reliable indicator at night of the identity of an animal is the way it moves. A particular episode that occurred on one dawn patrol illustrates both these identification features.

I was adjusting the shooting lamp, moving with the angle of the Landrover when we rounded a bend. All at once, a large, pat-terned animal—''a feline of sorts'' was our initial reaction—bolted from the scrub off the driver's side of the vehicle straight into the glare thrown by the lamp. Paul lurched to a halt just as it crossed over in front of us and, in the space of a heartbeat, loped off and away through the opposite flank of metre-high grass, its head appearing and reappearing above the grass for some seconds. If we hadn't seen the animal at close quarters, certainly the head repeatedly bobbing above the crown of the tall grass would have been a giveaway; it indicated the characteristic lope of a cheetah. Within a few minutes our eyes had completely lost sight of it, so black is the bush when far removed from the pervading artificial phosphorescence of civilisation. Significantly, the sighting occurred at a spot situated directly between the two reported sightings we'd had of King Cheetah, which were roughly three kilometres apart. Was the animal that crossed our path that night a King Cheetah? We never found out.

On our way back to camp with yet some distance to cover, we arrived at the dried-up riverbed of the Matobole, still little more than a crudely gouged-out drain after the dry. Several metres in width, it was a steep drop for the Landrover to negotiate. Climbing up out of it at an virtual 50% angle, we broached the top, and as the nose dropped horizontal again, a moving column of grey was revealed by the glare of our headlights. There were elephants unlimited, right, left and centre, with no room for an opening obvious anywhere; and the steep river-drop directly behind us didn't help either. Paul switched the headlights off and let the Landrover's engine idle gently, being the one vehicle of the two fortuitously blessed with an engine that almost purred. Our eyes searched among the dim shadows for an escape route. Minutes passed. Suddenly, what looked to be an opening appeared ahead. Easing the clutch out, and swallowing a "Hail Mary", Paul rocketed towards it. We couldn't be positive but the herd— possibly with young—numbered between thirty and forty. We didn't stop to count them but just kept on driving, packing enough adrenalin between us to supply a rugby team!

Daylight searches were quickly becoming a relief. A recent report had come our way of an old African claiming to have seen three oddly-marked cheetahs early one morning in the plains area of Tuli. He told Gulubane that he saw them from his donkey cart, clearly running together, and that they had definitely not been normally-marked cheetahs. The Madala had specifically sought us

130

Examining spoor at the Limpopo.

out to give us this news. At the first opportunity we set out to scour the entire area on foot over several days. One morning, quite early, while I stopped to reload my camera, Paul's attention was instinctively drawn to a patch of something about two hundred metres up ahead in the direction towards which we were walking. It is queer how in the bush one's senses become alive to the subtlest suggestion of a presence. We had a look through binoculars, but already the light of the day was glary and diffused, as it often is in the tropics, tending to muddle the view and confuse the eye. We edged closer, peering through the glasses as we did so. Then, as if sensing us, what had been just a huddle sprang to life as four animals loped off. They disappeared behind a nearby kopje, only to re-emerge on the crest which was now, by an amazing stroke of good fortune, less than a hundred metres from us.

They'd clearly not been alarmed by us. There was some distance between us and them and the wind was in our favour. Thus, four slender figures stood spotlighted against the azure skyline. They were cheetahs alright. But what sort of markings did they have? Through the binoculars they looked suspiciously heavy and dark. We needed to get closer. But the cheetahs had other ideas. As if reading our thoughts, they turned and left the kopje, trotting off instead along a line of dips and rises that took them ever-increasingly away from us. We followed as best we could, picking up their spoor, but they appeared to have little intention of staying in the area, moving as they were at a leisurely though purposeful pace. Eventually, at a sandy creekbed, we knew we had lost them. Some very clearly incised pug-prints here indicated three nearly adult cheetahs and one adult—a family group. We searched the plains area often after this but never found a trace of the foursome again.

Now and then we would come across the pug-mark of a solitary cheetah, sometimes of a lion, the pugs of the latter on one occasion measuring up to 30 centimetres across. Once we came across a fresh kill, only an hour or so old, near to where we had first seen the cheetahs. All that remained of a dog baboon was its skull and part of the rib-cage, to which shreds of skin and fur still clung. Our unheralded appearance at the kill disturbed a gathering of white-headed vultures. Far from handsome in repose, these carrion birds are a treat to watch when flying and soaring majestically, spiralling upwards on thermals, or just floating around in circles.

Once we followed a sound to beyond a rocky ridge—a curiously familiar, urban sound of the type that belongs in a railway yard, or on a construction site. Sounding just like heavy bars being banged together, the source of it was several minutes walk away, although it had seemed much closer at first, indeed almost on top

132

of us, a contradiction due, I dare say, to the quality of acoustics in the bush, where distant sounds may seem to be only inches away, as if in a music chamber. In the bush there is only one thing that can sound like that, the heavy clash of animal horn against animal horn. In this case it had to be big animal horn; it was the sound of a territorial battle. Picking our way over the rise, we came down behind some boulders... and there we found two huge eland bulls horn to horn. The greatest of the antelopes in more than just size, with the mysterious capacity to stop themselves sweating, getting so close to elands in the wild is rare, especially when they are rival bulls battling for supremacy. We watched from our rocky centre-court seat, a couple of metres away, for nearly 20 minutes until a lusty zebra stallion, a fellow spectator seemingly as gripped as we were by the duel, eventually got wind of us and let out its heart-thrilling peel of alarm. Herbivore to herbivore, such calls are absolutely imperative and so, reluctantly, the combatants turned from each other to trot away, their hooves clicking, their great dewlaps swinging from side to side like ponderous pendulums.

Tuli abounded in birdlife of a rich variety with reputedly over 350 different species. The camp and its environs made a birdwatcher's paradise. Strolling along the stretch of the Limpopo below the camp just before sundown each evening, when the geese would pass overhead, one could count plovers, coots and teal in careless abandon, and on occasion a stately heron standing motionless at the water's edge where the river was in flow, waiting to catch an unwary fish with a quick thrust of its bill. The wild, piercing clarion call of a fish eagle atop a lofty tree was unmistakeable. Flashily dressed in plumes of chalk-white, red and black, the fish eagle is one of Africa's most handsome and easily recognised birds of prey. Cormorants and the closely related darters thrived. And there was one peculiar-looking bird we would only see now and then fishing in the shallows for small fish and crabs, the hammerkop. With a head that is hammer-shaped in profile and seems to have no forehead at all, its slicked down head-feathers swept backwards give the impression of growing straight out of it's beak.

A tender, soporific cooing in camp announced that the gentle doves had arrived. Two varieties predominated, the red-eyed turtle dove and the laughing dove. In distinct contrast were the red-billed wood-hoopoes which would forage furiously through the bush around the camp in extraordinarily noisy parties. Searching the trunks and branches of trees for spiders and insects, they would hang upside-down in their enthusiasm as they assiduously probed the bark, cackling all the while amongst themselves. Noisier still were parties of little red-faced colies, their chubby round bodies and soft, fur-like feathers showing why they have acquired their alternative name of "mousebirds". Not a day went by when we weren't visited by a lone crested barbet, displaying colours so intricately woven it could well have sprung out of a Venetian tapestry or an ancient vase from Rhodes. It was so tame after many months fraternising with us in camp that it was very nearly eating out of our hands.

There was no shortage of game-birds either, not a day going by without a covey of the ubiquitous guinea-fowl, or francolins (the quail of Africa), pounding off down a path in front of us in a berserk display of feathers and dust. Guinea-fowl particularly, in their neat plumes of an almost Victorian respectability, their thin legs taking precise little steps, always put one in mind of a bevy of prim old dames hurrying off to town. Somehow the go-away birds, prattling and clumsily clambering about the tops of tall thorn trees, seemed to belie their nasal cry "khoe-weyyyy". I couldn't help feeling a certain empathy with this attractive clown of the long tail feathers and crest, however much it chose to disrupt the most intimate moments!

For exotically-coloured birds, Tuli, and more especially the area immediately around the camp, was a bird photographer's dream. Here could be seen daintily pastelled waxbills, no bigger than a wren; lilac-breasted rollers, those avian opals; luminous sunbirds like iridescent jewels dipping curved beaks into suppliant flowers; bee-eaters by the dozen, the European and swallow-tailed feeding on dragonflies, the rainbow patterned white-fronted, and most notable of all the carmine, moving in small colonies and trans-

134

Approach to Mashatu through open bush. The Landrover's special 'sand' paintwork
blends with the surrounding.

forming the look of the land with a flash of wings; and paradise
flycatchers were well represented in densely-foliaged places, the
crested heads of both sexes being regally adorned in shades of
deepest blue, with the male's sweeping tail, burnished orange, a
conspicuous sight amid the lush greenery they liked to shelter in.
Here and there one would come upon weaver bird nests dangling
like hanging baskets from the tips of palm fronds. In Tuli, these
skillfully crafted nests belonged to two species of weaver, the red-
headed and the masked, with the male of each the homemaker,
gallantly building nest after nest until he has won his heart's
delight.

Kingfishers frequented the waters below the camp. A work of art
in turquoise and sapphire blue, the tiny malachite kingfisher would
perch on a root jutting out from an eroded riverbank. Its bigger
cousin, the black-and-white plumed pied kingfisher, had the habit
of returning with a fresh catch to a favourite perch against which
it would proceed to beat its unfortunate prey so as to soften it
before swallowing it whole ... always with the head first so the

135

seales lay flat for a smooth passage. And who could ever forget the sight of the jaunty hoopoe sauntering about in the open? On seeing one for the first time in India (for Indian ones look the same) I was reminded of an identical bird with dashing black-and-white striped wings, russet chest and head, topped by a majestic crest as showy as any ceremonial headress, which had been painted long ago from life on the wall of a dignitary's tomb in the Egypt of the Pharaohs. In Tuli, as in India, it was like looking at an ancient artefact come to life; a link in an unbroken chain which stretched back four thousand years and beyond.

Man-eater

It was the time of the snakes, the dizzy months prior to New Year, and they had nearly gone before it even began to dawn on us how much some of the few black people in the area were coming to rely on us for medicine; for the basic, bush *materia medica* no expedition can afford to be without. There was a dearth of proper medical aid nearby. The Lodge was limited. The first-aid supplies at Tuli's government game scout camp were even more basic than ours, with the nearest first-aid post inside Botswana nearly a hundred kilometres away at a place called Bobonong. Locals could go across the border into South Africa, to the cottage hospital in Alldays; but this seemed to be an experience worse than the illness. One particular incident illustrates the problem well.

An elderly African woman and her grandaughter, were severely bitten by a snake in the night in the old lady's kaia; by the time proper medical treatment was sought, however, some six hours had elapsed. When we caught up with the story it was at the Lodge an hour later where an argument was in full swing over the apparent near-comatose forms of the old woman and young girl, both stretched out in an open Landrover ready to be driven across to Alldays for treatment.

Someone was insisting a puff adder had been responsible, judging by the look of the bites. The old woman on the other hand, drowsy though coherent, was adamant it had been a cobra. Oddly enough, both victims had been bitten on the same arm, in the same place, with the affected zone just above the wrist heavily swollen and inflamed and their hands virtually unrecognisable as such. This was, indeed, a reaction consistent with a puff adder bite. But in a hut, at night, even supposing that they had flung their arms out straight as they slept on pallets laid flat on the floor, it did not seem probable. With a very potent tissue-destroying venom, one snake packing enough to kill five men within 24 hours—sooner when

137

untreated—puff adders account for more deaths in Africa than any other snake. Indeed, so feared is its bite, some Africans have been known to die of shock at the actual moment of being struck by one! Regardless of the swelling, however, and bearing in mind the elder victim's insistence that she had been bitten by a cobra—even though with a cobra bite there is very little local reaction round the wound—the circumstances did not suggest that the bites were the work of a puff adder. For one thing, puff adders, unlike cobras, generally keep out of doors. Then we hit upon a possible solution. Certainly it would account for the six-hour time lapse, Africans not being casual about anything to do with snakes. Isangoma—the witchdoctor—had applied his art, spending several hours prodding, probing and pricking the wounds and applying various concoctions and ointments, and thus accounting for the most of the swelling and inflammation.

Cobra venom, like that of the mambas, is neurotoxic and just as deadly, affecting the nervous system with resultant muscular retardation leading to breathing difficulty and eventual heart failure. But cobras are timid snakes and can on occasion strike clumsily, their fangs not penetrating deeply enough to inject more than a little venom. Opening its mouth as it moves into strike, the cobra extends long fangs with which it literally stabs its victim before closing its mouth to bite, forcing a mighty dose of venom deep into the wound, the pressure of the bite ramming it through in one generous spurt. If the strike is clumsy and the snake doesn't get a firm grip, the pressure of the bite is reduced, thereby affecting the amount of venom injected. Symptoms would therefore be milder than usual. In fact there are cases of poisonous snake-bite where no symptons develop, indicating that no venom has been injected. Thus, many ''cures'' are merely the consequence of a lucky quirk of fate. The old lady and her grandaughter eventually got to Alldays where, after further frustrations over the identity of the snake responsible, the old lady's opinion was finally heeded, and cobra antivenin was applied. The patients pulled through in spite of the drama that had surrounded them for nearly ten hours. In the meantime a snake had been flushed out of the woman's kaia and despatched forthwith. It was an Egyptian cobra, one of two species of cobra found at Tuli.

We never had any serious alarms with snakes ourselves, possibly due to the rains coming early, snakes generally being most active just prior to the wet when the land is at its driest (though in parts of Africa where the winters are mild, as at Tuli, they may not be very active). They were certainly around though and included pythons, Egyptian and spitting cobras, puff adders, the more "dangerous" black mambas, and the less aggressive boomslangs the venom of which reputedly constitute, drop for drop, one of the most potent venoms known in Africa. Fortunately the poison glands are relatively small, which is why the antivenin is very difficult to obtain in quantity and why successful bites, the snakes being back-fanged, are quite rare. The deadliest snake of all, the gaboon viper, I believe we were too far west to encounter.

Semolale cattle-post comprises a sleepy smattering of mud-huts that seems to quiver and shimmer as it lays caught in a heat haze some forty kilometres west beyond the Tuli "back line" or Vet Cordon boundary. For a few brief days it was to enjoy a rare notoriety. When the first bit of news came through to us we were doubtful because this was, after all, uninspiring cattle country, although admittedly cattle can be alluring to the larger predators! Two men claiming to have seen a King Cheetah at the post had reported the sighting to a district policeman, a lone authority of sorts in the area, who immediately put them in his Landcruiser and drove the considerable distance to our camp at Tuli so that they could give us the news at first-hand. That, in itself, gave their story a kind of credibility, not that we doubted their sincerity. Gulubane certainly thought their story had merit. But we had learned how easy it is for people, however sincere they may be (and rural Africans usually are), to be outrageously wide of the mark when reporting sightings of unusual animals.

What nagged at us in this instance was the nature of the area, the land and vegetation type, the fact that it was country given over to cattle and all that that meant in the development of housing and the blocking of age-old migratory routes, leaving little if any wild

139

game there as a result. There may have been lions, but surely not King Cheetahs! We were still wondering whether or not to follow up the report when a visit from Peter and Samson, the local resident government game scouts, inadvertently made our minds up for us. Unaware themselves of the reported King Cheetah sighting, they had received in the meantime another message over the scout's radio. This stated simply that a tribesman had been attacked and eaten by a lioness at Semolale. The priority for them in their capacity as government game scouts, was to track the animal down and shoot it. A man-eater on the loose couldn't be ignored. Paul had a reputation as a marksman so they had called to ask him if he would accompany them on the hunt, to play "bwana", so to speak. The victim had been badly mauled, we were told, and most of his stomach and one leg had been eaten. The lioness had attacked him in thick thorn scrub and there was every reason to believe she was in the bloom of health.

That man-eating lions are almost invariably mangy, tooth-worn cripples is quite inaccurate. Experience has shown that most are sleek, fit and generally big. Lions may become man-eaters for a number of reasons: accident, inheritance, or sheer hunger. Thousands upon thousands of people have been eaten by man-eaters over the decades. Natural disasters, or the custom of many tribes not to bury their dead but to discard them in the bush has been an obvious encouragement to the lions. Nowadays, the upsurge in tourism to game parks has helped dampen the lion's inbred fear of man, thus increasing rather than decreasing the possibility of it becoming a man-eater. Unarmed we are, after all, a pushover compared with the lion's usual prey. What should not be overlooked is that once a big feline has tasted human flesh—for whatever reason, as in the case of the Semolale man-eater—it may well choose to keep man permanently on the menu. With this is mind Paul opted to take his 12-bore with solid shot, the best weapon to use when trailing thin-skinned animals in thick cover. At the cattle-post there was a vague feeling of unconcern about the man-eater incident. There seemed to be even less concern for its partially-eaten victim! He'd been driven in the back of an open

Study of the common cheetah in successive moods.

truck over 100 kilometres westwards on an hours-long, gruelling journey along a bush track that was no more than an incision in the open bush, firstly to the small dispensary at Bobonong, which could do little for him, thence onto the more substantial Selibi Phikwe, his last hope. But here his chances of survival were pronounced as slim, the treatment he required being of a sophisticated nature beyond the means of the small bush hospital. No, it wasn't concern he aroused. Rather, the episode seemed to serve as an excuse for a good deal of thigh-slapping humour! That amazing African fatalism in operation again. Indeed, though the prospect of killing a lion or a lioness, man-eater or not, generally galvanises

141

Africans into a near-paroxysm of excitement, it was the King Cheetah that now appeared to evoke the greater interest. But no-one was able to substantiate the mens' reported sighting. We were unable to winkle out any old stories surrounding possible past sightings or like incidents. We had no spoor to follow and no remains of a kill to work on. Possessed of no magic formula for finding King Cheetahs in the wild, we couldn't even rely on the accepted norms of search. Even with ordinary cheetahs we had had little success in three months to date, having spotted no more than ten individuals, singly or in groups (one never being certain how many are repeats).

The trip to Semolale made us question our need to remain any longer in Botswana. Nowhere did our search for the King Cheetah seem more hopeless than out there in that spiritless country where the ankole, the cattle that bear the longest horns of any domestic stock, reign supreme. Lifeblood of Botswana's economy, the cow is arguably the greatest threat to Africa's free-roaming wildlife. West beyond Tuli, at any rate, one could believe this to be true. Perhaps the threat of the cow was even more insidious than the threat of the poacher, the major difference being that poaching offends more conventions.

Wire traps, or noose snares, work like garottes. Vulgarly unsophisticated death-dealers, they trap a wide variety of animals and are the means by which many an emaciated cripple is left to hobble in the bushes, enduring a slow, painful death as a crude strip of fence wire cuts deeper and deeper into putrefying flesh with every movement. A rhino with its head almost severed from its shoulders struggles for days in a living hell made more agonising by the hideous wrench of scavenging jaws on its intestines. A kudu bull of mighty crown, with its rump viciously wrapped in a wire noose which will eventually cut it in two, stops itself collapsing by propping itself up against a shaded tree. A few metres or less of strip wire formed into a slip-knot, with the free end slung from a strong branch and anyone can make a snare. It's as simple as that. Simple, but deadly.

A casually browsing antelope will put its head through one and be

142

none the wiser till the moment it tries to move away; the knot slips, the noose contracts, tightening round the animal's neck or shoulders, depending on its size. The intervention of lion or leopard would be a merciful release. Wire loop snares are also left to lay surreptitiously at ground level, ready to ambush any unsuspecting grazer. No vertebrate is immune, from the smallest to the largest. Elsewhere in the African bush one finds more complicated contrivances, such as spring nooses, bow traps, drop spears and gin-traps. For all their simplicity, however, the makeshift wire snares we came across in Tuli occasionally were just as lethal; and certainly they inflicted a more lingering death. Crude fence wire born of cattle barriers is as devastating in its implications as any sophisticated trap of today.

One bewildered victim we came across would have been better dead, an elephant with its trunk literally wrenched from its body, a spectacle not easily forgotten. The massive form was bent double over the water's edge, forcing its mouth down to drink in an ineffectual, painfully laborious manner utterly foreign to it. The lifeline of the mighty, the sensitive, the sensible elephant is its trunk. It is its hand and its nose. It uses it to drink, to smell, to touch and caress, to carry food to its mouth; to blow dust and water over itself to cool down and relieve the biting of insects ... as well as for fun and hi-jinks. Trundling through the bush, it will use its trunk to part the way through thick undergrowth or overhanging foliage, or to feed. Either way, if in the process its trunk slips through a wire loop snare hanging secretly in the vegetation, the elephant will instinctively pull away from it. Though foot traps are notorious claimants of elephants it is the wire noose snare hung from a tree that inflicts the more severe injury, cutting and cutting into the trunk until finally the organ drops off.

On seeing such an animal one wants only to put it out of its misery, but this is forbidden by law in some areas where only official government rangers have the authority to do so. And with good reason too. Poachers would have a field-day. By claiming that the animal had been fatally hurt they would have a ready-made excuse for killing wholesale on ''humanitarian grounds''. Nature's apparent disregard for suffering all too frequently shocks our human sensibilities. Suffice it to say that she has her ways. When it was time for us to leave Tuli, the trunkless elephant was still there. Life—on any terms it seems—is sweet.

We began to consider our future plans. The hunt for a skull and skins remained a priority. We toyed with the idea of returning overland to Europe via the Okavango, Zambia and Malawi initially, picking up whatever news we could of the King Cheetah, past and present. The prospect of uncovering some arcane reference to the King Cheetah among Egypt's treasury of ancient legend and lore was most attractive. Like the Sumerians a thousand years earlier, the pharaohs in the dynastic period between BC 1600 and 1200 had kept and hunted with cheetahs.

Man has enjoyed the companionship of cheetahs throughout history. Marco Polo writes of visiting Kublai Khan at Karakorum, the site of his summer residence, where he kept up to a thousand cheetahs for hunting purposes. Indeed, as hunting companions for over five thousand years for some of the great and powerful potentates of history, cheetahs have occupied a niche more special than even that of the elephant or the horse. The special relationship has continued until recent times, with the rajahs of India, the sherifs and sheikhs of North Africa and Arabia showing a fondness for these animals. Like the khans and noyons of Mongol-ruled Asia, the Moghul Akbar also kept a number of them. Russian princes hunted with them, as did certain of the French kings, the Syrians and the Palestinians. Even William the Conqueror and Emperor Leopold I of Austria had their own cheetahs. Such a long and special relationship between man and cheetah may account for the reputation the cheetah has of never attacking man. Certainly there is nothing on record to suggest that it will do so.

None of our research had led us to an ancient reference concerning an unusually marked cat in any way resembling a King Cheetah. With such a depth of association across five thousand years between man and cheetah, the existence of a bigger cheetah, a cheetah so strikingly handsome, so different to its still enigmatic cousin yet bearing all of its charisma, could surely not have gone

144

unnoticed. It was an omission that not for the first time made us stop and think. But now, with the experience of months of fieldwork behind us, something was different; the perspective had altered, and it was to set us on course for a radical change of thinking.

In the meantime, having made the conscious decision to leave Tuli, a breathless feeling of valediction, as if our senses didn't quite know what to make of it, quickly settled upon us. Ironically, we now found ourselves being urged to stay on. We had offers of light planes, even a helicopter. A businessman from the south, with an interest in the area, flew up in his private plane and tried to persuade us to give the place another go. In his opinion, finding a King Cheetah in such a charming, unsung corner of Africa would open it up as a tourist haven, attracting monied clientèle in search of something different. We did not share his sentiments. There are only vestiges of wilderness remaining. Once man has encroached upon these there will then be nowhere for the herds to retreat. Many of the more elusive animals now live in places where man seldom penetrates, in a bid to remain just that—elusive.

Our reaction to all this, in the eleventh hour, was to conclude that life at times displays an appalling degree of bad timing and it were best to leave it at that. And so we celebrated Christmas, New Year and my birthday all at the same time and prepared to leave Tuli. We made arrangements for Gulubane to get in touch with us via radio, telegram—smoke signal—come what may, should he hit on any significant news of the King Cheetah, whether live animals or skins. He had already left us when, during the following week, we took our leave of Tuli and crossed the border into South Africa, "Lulu" and "Ingwe" having been washed free of months of caked-on dust and grime in the Limpopo, ready to start afresh. Another Africa was calling.

A Once... or Future King

Apart from a remarkable continuity in the standard pattern of three broad dorsal stripes, a preponderance of heavy, irregular blotches far larger than any ordinary cheetah's spots, and a striped and ringed tail in all known King Cheetah specimens, research has otherwise shown that outstanding pattern or colour variation in the ordinary cheetah is rare, with no intermediate coat pattern between it and the King Cheetah evident. Of course, smaller or paler spotting in the ordinary cheetah does occur, environmental conditions demanding it. Spotted cheetahs from Namibia, for example, are very often far paler than ordinary cheetahs from, say, East Africa. A select number of cheetahs known to have been living several years ago in the cold, arid reaches of north-west Iran and strictly protected by the Shah's government, had very long hair. From populations of the two races of cheetah—, the African, and the now drastically depleted Asiatic cheetah—a number of sub-species has been described by taxonomists. Six of them have been described from Africa where the only large cheetah populations remain. The differences, however, are not altogether clear. Physically at any rate, they in no way compare with the distinct differences existing between *Acinonyx rex* and *A. jubatus*, in which we are not only talking about a complete change from a flat, monotonous pattern of small coin-spots to a thickly furred pelage laced with inky, fulvous blotches and heavy, broad stripes (not to mention the change of markings always on the tail), but also about different colouring and length of hair. By our reckoning, too, based on a close examination of skins, which may be distorted in the process of preparing them, the King Cheetah appeared to be larger. Apart from an hypothesis that the King Cheetah is a developing melanistic variant, the only reports from fairly authoritative sources of notable coat variations (excluding those of *A. rex*), were unsubstantiated by skins or photographs. There were

146

two accounts from Africa this century of black (or melanistic) cheetahs; there was a somewhat muddled report of "partial-albinism" in the "woolly cheetah"; and there was a much earlier reference to a Moghul ruler in India, a renowned "naturalist" of his day, Jahangir, being presented with a "white cheetah" at Agra, the first and only one he ever saw, so he tells us. "Its spots" he wrote, "were of blue colour". What is notable about the reference is that the appearance of the animal obviously impressed our royal Moghul commentator enough for him to record its existence for posterity. How noteworthy, then, would a cat as magnificently marked as a King Cheetah have seemed to Jahangir, and other keepers of great kennels of cheetahs in Asia, the Near East and North Africa alike in previous centuries. We can only assume that no-one had ever seen one, given the lack of early pictorial or written references to such a cat.

This dearth of historical records of an animal even remotely like the King Cheetah during the five thousand years man and cheetah have been associated, notably in the hunt as evidenced by ancient drawings, was worth more than just a passing thought. Was it a recently developed, abnormal variant of the cheetah? Had we, like others, for too long been caught in the trap of always looking backwards rather than forwards, bogged down so to speak by notions of throwback, recessive mendelian mutation, and all that? Did the answer lie not so much in the past but in the future? After all, how else would an evolving new strain of cheetah start except as a mutation, as an aberration?

Certainly, the more our research developed, the more and more substantial did the King Cheetah begin to look. The months of research and field-work in Botswana, for instance, though yielding nothing tangible in the way of live King Cheetahs, had added five previously unrecorded ones to the existing list of King Cheetah pelts. For various reasons the other four—the mysterious "Red Shields skin", the one reputedly hanging on a homestead wall, the two auctioned in South Africa—we felt did not justify inclusion in the list. Thus, with the five from Botswana, the pelt collected in the Honde and given to the local Native Commissioner, and another

King Cheetah skin from Zimbabwe, now in the collection of the Kaffrarian Museum King Williams Town, South Africa, showing the ravages of years spent as a floor rug chewed by dogs.

traced from Rhodesia to the Kaffrarian Museum, King William's Town (where it was purchased for a mere £15 after being used as a floor rug chewed by dogs), the list had risen to a respectable nineteen, never previously having exceeded a dozen for decades.

Having taken our leave of Botswana our efforts, far from drying up, continued to produce results. We traced seven more skins, for example, one of which had been "lost" for almost forty years. Three of them, curiously enough, had been listed previously as one skin. We were delighted that each skin unfailingly showed the typical King Cheetah pattern but, at the same time, we regretted the needless slaughter.

At Pietersburg, hub of the northern Transvaal bushveld, we made camp on the outskirts of town. A misnomer really, Pietersburg is not so much a town as a big, rambling village that, like some sophisticated "wild west" watering hole, grew to fit the needs of local farming gentry and travellers alike. A friendly place,

148

Pietersburg had a community which preferred old habits, like shooting for sport, to "academic" notions of conservation. Only by directing our enquiries towards skin traders, hunters, even poachers, rather than naturalists—if there were any indeed—were we likely to be assured of any success in a search for skins. There was the ivory dealer, for instance, who believed he'd seen King Cheetah pelts for sale on the Zaire/Zambia border near a place called Ndola and again at a lush spot in the Zambezi reaches not far from the Victoria Falls. Although these localities agreed with the type of well-covered terrain we'd come to consider as the King Cheetah's favoured country it is as well to remember that pelts can travel hundreds of miles, with poachers and migrant workers, from where they were actually collected. A private tour of his factory certainly knocked on the head, for us at least, erstwhile assurances of reductions in the wholesale slaughter of elephants across Africa to date, with truckloads of raw tusks arriving from "somewhere up north" and ivory curiosities being churned out even as we gazed. Suddenly tales of heavy elephant poaching still going on even in Rhodesia's Wankie National Park, one of Africa's premier reserves where elephants were reputed to be present in thousands before the war, no longer seemed so improbable.

Instead of concentrating concern on a general campaign to root out large-scale poaching at source the western world has aimed at halting the importation of ivory, spotted skins and the like from Africa. This policy has pushed values of ivory, animal horn and skins sky high; the protests of conservation bodies, by comparison, seem to be little more than hollow, conscience-salving exercises reaching no further than the glossy-magazines and colour television. Indeed, outside of freebooters such as the ivory dealer, there was little that conservation bodies in general knew, let alone could advance on the subject of the King Cheetah. At least, on the unholy question of skins, hunters and taxidermists were far more reliable sources of information. Piet, the professional taxidermist involved in the muddled issue of the Alldays cheetahs hadn't had a single King Cheetah pelt pass through his hands in all his years of experience. And some experience that was! For me, his airy, squeaky-clean Pietersburg studio was a revelation. The needs of research and education aside, I have never liked stuffed animals, my experience of dusty, expressionless Victorian specimens without aesthetic appeal having seen to that. But this man had made taxidermy come alive, so to speak. From tiny elephant shrews to Cape buffalo Piet had captured the spirit of his animals, at least giving dignity back where there was no longer life.

Over lunch at Pietersburg's main hotel, the hunter who'd accompanied us to Piet's studio had a story for us. Lulu, as we came to know him, had been in Mozambique, on his last shoot there just prior to independence. He had been working the dense, secluded bush country hugging the border with Zimbabwe, some 50 kilometres north of a place called Vila de Manica. Interestingly enough this place is adjacent to the Pungwe/Honde area, our projected zone of search in the aborted Rhodesian exercise. It was here he had shot a King Cheetah, not knowing at the time so he said, what it was. Spurious excuse or not, it's a story you hear often enough. He described the incident. He'd been carefully making his way upwind along a dry riverbed, peering through its dappled flanks for game; he had a licence for kudu and buffalo only and the area promised plenty of both. Through a cluster of trees that kept him well hidden from view he caught sight of a large cat—a large, dark cat he couldn't readily identify—lying on top of a rocky ledge sunning itself. He gazed, watching it intently, not moving an inch. Downwind of it, and well hidden behind a guard of trees, he watched a little longer; the big cat seemed completely oblivious of his presence. It was, he assured us, too good an opportunity to miss, licence or no licence. He took aim, eyes narrowing on his target. As he did so, a most uncanny thing happened. In that breathless instant, as he squeezed the trigger, the cat's head turned, as if drawn by some extra-sensory perception and stared straight in his direction. Here Lulu broke off his narrative and gazed intently into each of our faces in turn, as if seeking some precise explanation, some logical answer; but there wasn't one forthcoming from us. This incident shook him, he told us, like nothing else he'd ever known and for a fleeting moment he seemed to lose all sense of

150

what he was doing. But it was only for a moment. There came the tell-tale thud, as ordained; the fine head fell forward and the lights of those questing eyes went out. This reminded me of a man who had been an amateur hunter all his life until the day he suddenly hung up his guns, never to hunt an animal again for sport. It is an unspoken rule never to rush up to the animal as soon as one's shot has dropped it but to wait until it has stopped kicking, when its muscles have ceased flinching and contracting to a notable degree. For it can be an unnerving sight. This man had just hit a kudu, a male with a fine set of horns, but unfortunately had not placed his shot as neatly as he might have. In its last throes the frantic animal had run on, ending up hopelessly enmeshed in a wire fence. Impulsively rushing up to it, the man saw something he would never forget: tears, welling from the stately antelope's eyes as they soulfully gazed back at him. The fact that the hunter knew perfectly well that animals on the brink of death expel water from their eyes was neither here nor there. For the first time in his life he questioned his need to hunt. In those eyes he met himself. Lulu learned from his companions after the cat had been skinned that he had shot a Rhodesian cheetah, a King Cheetah, a cat certified as royal game. Well meaning and affable though he was, his "youthful impetuosity" excuse was not very convincing. Hardly notable either was the way the pelt had been cured; and the paws had been hacked off. What was notable for us, at least, was the animal's provenance. The close proximity of it to the virgin Pungwe/Honde area added greatly to the notion that King Cheetahs, because of their dark, heavy patterning were better suited to a well-wooded, lush terrain, adapting themselves in time, as it were, to a more secluded environment occasioned by man's ruthless appropriation of the open habitats of old (the root cause of the ordinary cheetah's rapid decline in numbers this century). An adherence to relatively secluded terrain, merging from semi-tropical rain forest, through thorn forest and thorn bush of acacias and euphorbias, to woodland habitats, such as one finds in the wide sweep of country stretching westwards from Mozambique across the Eastern Highlands and south-east of Zimbabwe to Tuli,

151

would certainly account for so few sightings of King Cheetahs down the years.

An adjunct to this which deserves to be mentioned is, of course, the increased leopard-threat-factor in such an environment, bearing in mind that leopards have been known to kill cheetahs. Dr. U. de V. Pienaar, Warden of Kruger Park, once showed us a particularly fine photograph he had in his possession by way of example. On balance the leopard probably poses no greater threat to the King Cheetah than do predator-competitors to ordinary cheetahs sharing savanna areas in normal conditions where man's encroachment has not dramatically altered the equilibrium. Without doubt the fact that we were known to be studying the King Cheetah, the cheetah with a difference, was exciting more and more attention.

Checking, for instance, the patterning on ordinary cheetahs for the appearance of stripes didn't produce evidence of even a close approach on any (let alone a row of spots joining to form a line) in almost two hundred cats examined. Cheetah sanctuaries, like the one run by urbane author Des Varaday at Loskopdam south of Pietersburg, offered ample opportunity for such study. For someone clearly fascinated by cheetahs in general, it came as no great surprise to us that he might also have harboured the hope of one day "breeding" a King from his stock of ordinary cheetahs. He did have one intriguing snippet of news for us. Once, in Blantyre, the commercial capital of Malawi, he had seen, among all the brouhaha and colour of a native market, an old African wearing what looked to him exactly like a King Cheetah skin! Regrettably, as is so often the way of things, he didn't follow it up, being about some other business at the time. With its rich blend of secluded mountain country and forest vegetation who was to say King Cheetah couldn't be in Malawi?

Of course, as has already been made clear, it doesn't necessarily follow that the locale where an animal skin is marketed is the same as its provenance. Just as predators will wander well beyond a prescribed habitat, nothing in nature being so cut and dried as to prevent it, so too in the skin trade a pelt may travel some considerable distance—poaching being commonly the reason—before it's eventually marketed. In our research, for example, some places where King Cheetah skins had been bought and sold just could not be considered synonymous with their provenance. The dry Makgadikgadi, that wonder of salt pans and desert scrub in the northern Kalahari, and Freeman's set of four pelts, of which three mysteriously "disappeared", illustrates this perfectly. Intelligent assessment in research is paramount if one is to make any sense of it, especially in an exercise of the kind we were engaged in, with its many variables. In this respect extant skins with an authenticated history and those without one presented special problems. A rumour, for example, of three skins in a curio shop in Pretoria that surfaced within hours of our departure for Tuli provided, when confirmed, a tantalising footnote to tales of vanished skins and those others, like the "Red Shields" pelt, we'd been unable to verify or trace. Apparently, since their collection, they had been sealed between layers of naphthalene in the same flat boxes at Ivy's Curios; and so there was no question about their high quality; they were in an exceptionally fine condition. Their origins, however, were questionable. During our months of absence in Tuli some preliminary investigations had been undertaken on our behalf. Rex Sevenoaks, actor, bon viveur and contact-man in Johannesburg, had made the initial approaches and, with wildlife artist Paul Bosman, had managed to get a sight of the skins. Ivy, the director of the firm seemed to be mildly secretive about their existence as much as about their origins. Apart from permitting Bosman to measure and sketch the pelts, he did not give much away about them. Although little could be ascertained through valid inquiry some information was available visually. Each pelt was as big as it was beautiful, the colours rich and vibrant, the pelage lush and silky with little stretching evident. With two males and one female the three averaged out at 7ft 2ins (2.16m) from nose to tail-tip, the largest just topping 7ft 8ins. By any estimate these had been big cheetahs. These pelts justified what many of the facts were indicating: the King Cheetah was king in more than just name. The best information we could establish about the provenance of the skins was that all three came from "somewhere" in eastern Botswana, arriving at the shop separately in, roughly, "1960, 1965 and 1966'. It was, in truth, an inquiry that occasioned much evasion. But it was not so with another skin.

For many years the whereabouts of a certain King Cheetah skin— noted for being the only one to date to come from South Africa— appeared unknown to sources of official King Cheetah research, Smithers among them. For this reason it became known as the "lost Messina skin". The story goes that in 1940 a King Cheetah was shot on a farm called Kongo in the vicinity of Messina, a town in the extreme north of the northern Transvaal, situated some 100 kilometres east of Tuli and just 15 kilometres from the border with Zimbabwe. The region impresses one as being ideal King Cheetah country, with woodland vegetation giving way to more heavy, lush cover the further east and north into Mozambique and Zimbabwe one goes, or west to Tuli. In the course of conversation Ivy, our host and owner of the special set of skins we had come to view, unwittingly supplied a surprise ending to the story of the "lost Messina skin".

In 1940, while still a callow apprentice learning the unedifying ins and outs of the family curio business, he had accompanied his father on a visit to a farm in the Transvaal. The farmer had just shot a large predator that had been worrying his livestock for some time but had been unable to identify it exactly. Ivy's father had no such difficulty: he recognised the unique pattern of the rare King Cheetah immediately. Offering to undertake the work personally, he advised that the skin be professionally cured with just the head mounted, appropriately, in the classic rampant style, snarling. The pelt in question was the "Messina King" of Kongo Farm.

In 1940, taxidermists had not yet begun to use fibreglass skulls for mounting purposes in place of the real thing and this, for us, raised one intriguing, very important question: had the original skull been used to mount the head of the "Messina King", or had the skull of an ordinary cheetah been used?

Ivy didn't deliberate long. His father had "definitely used the original skull" he told us; it was standard policy. If the skeleton

154

and/or skull of an animal had been retained, as was so in the case of the Kongo specimen, they would automatically be used in mounting the cured pelt if something a little more substantial than just a flat skin was desired. Authenticity and simple economics demanded it. In the case of a King Cheetah skin, its sheer exclusiveness was motive enough. This information produced a sense of exuberance in Paul and I which is difficult to describe.

The late Mr Robert Boulton Ivy with the Ivys' fine collection of three King Cheetah skins. (By kind permission of the Ivy family)

For years the question of the existence of *Acinonyx rex* skulls had been bandied about. In at least two instances skulls have been cited as being those of the King Cheetah, only to be confirmed later as those of the ordinary cheetah. Lord Walter Rothschild had been so anxious to obtain a skull of *rex* for his collection at Tring that he had offered a reward for one; but none had materialised. There is a skull preserved in the Field Museum, Chicago, which for many years was reputed to be that of *rex* and was even officially recorded

155

The Kongo Farm King Cheetah specimen from Messina (South Africa) with mounted head containing the original skull, the first King Cheetah specimen officially recorded outside Zimbabwe. 'Lost' to science for forty years, it is in the possession of Mr Jan Jourbert of Krugersdorp, South Africa.

as such by such authorities as Austin Roberts. Another was said to have been housed in the Queen Victoria Museum at Salisbury, Rhodesia, but this was little more than a rumour. An authentic King Cheetah skull would, indeed, have been a worthy acquisition, for if it showed a marked difference from the ordinary cheetah we would have been that much closer to establishing the King Cheetah's taxonomic status. Now that we were aware the original skull had been used in the mounting of the Messina skin, a search for its present owner and whereabouts took priority over everything, including that long overland trip to Egypt.

We had two names to work on: Van der Walt, the original owner, and a second Afrikaans name, Van der Westhuizen, that had come to Ivy in a flash of inspiration. Thus armed, the course we should follow seemed perfectly logical, to us at least, seeing that we were in the Transvaal, that state of staunch Afrikaner nationhood founded on farming and gold where the Boer's descendants cherish and exercise their right to vote and to own the land they work. We would examine the voters' roll! If this failed, we reassured ourselves, there was always the Police!

Optimistic as ever we made good our intentions by first taking ourselves off to Nationalist Party headquarters, hub of Afrikaner political fervour. Here, once they'd decided we were harmless enough, the people were politeness itself. Patiently drawing out the words slowly in that simple manner people adopt when speaking to unfortunates, they explained that the names Van der Walt and Van der Westhuizen were among the commonest in South Africa. Well, after about a day of this, the obvious solution finally dawned on us (being so long in the bush had doubtless dulled our wits): we'd plead our case to the Press! Amazingly enough, within 24 hours of approaching *Beeld*, one of the more enterprising and liberal of the Afrikaans-language dailies with a good circulation in the Transvaal, we'd located the skin!

Three responses cross-referenced the same location, Krugersdorp, a small town about 30 kilometres from the centre of Johannesburg. According to the reports, the "lost Messina skin" formed part of the collection of a trophy hunter by the name of Jan Jourbert, who it seems had had it for almost twenty years. Twenty years... and just 30 kilometres from Johannesburg—so much for previous research! We pulled up in a press car outside of a trophy room built as a huge, white-washed brick rondavel adjoining the main house. Inside was a home-made natural history museum of luxurious, airy proportions; by the time my dazzled eyes had become adjusted to the scene Paul had located the skin.

Classically edged in green baize, it lay draped across a table, the head definitely erect and snarling. Without the benefit of being enclosed under glass, it had suffered from being exposed for decades. The lush depth of fur and rich colouring long associated with the King Cheetah had noticeably been diminished, the pelage thinning as dramatically as the typically striking, black-brown and cream markings had faded to a musty chocolate on a yellowing background. Be that as it may, the distinctive jigsaw pattern of the King Cheetah still impressed at a glance. More than that, from what Jourbert had to tell us, and not unbefitting the King's special

157

brand of uniqueness, this particular individual had died in quite remarkable circumstances—remarkable, that is, for a cheetah.

Midnight at a lion-bait and Van der Walt—a long-time friend of Jourbert's—watched from his hide as a large cat emerged from the shadowy bush beyond the stake. Never striking in daylight, a predator had been troubling his stock for months. Assuming it to be a lion, or at least a lioness or immature male because of the size of the calves he had lost, Van der Walt had staked out the carcass of a full-grown cow in a last-ditch attempt to draw the cat out. It did, with one result. Van der Walt had been convinced, even as he'd fired, that what he'd seen emerge from the bush, deliberate a moment, and then move across to the bait, was a lion, thereby recalling those observations at night of King Cheetahs mistaken for lions.

Midnight. Lion-bait. A King Cheetah shot. Exceptional circumstances indeed, circumstances which postulate—when one considers how much of a moot point is the fact of the ordinary cheetah hunting at night, let alone its going to bait—one important question: how much of a cheetah is this King Cheetah? A little? A lot? With the attributes of a leopard maybe? Or is it simply very much its own cat, as different in habit from the ordinary cheetah, if the lion-bait episode is anything to go by, as it is in physical appearance? Even the richly wooded country around Messina excites comment, tucked as it is into the lusher traces of the northern curve of the Limpopo where the river forms the border with Zimbabwe. This consistency in habitat choice was reflected in an interesting sidelight on our meeting with Jourbert, an observation made to us by his geologist son-in-law that was compatible with the ivory dealer's claim of having seen King Cheetah pelts for sale in Zambia. Working on contract there for a number of years prior to his marriage, he was once in a place called Mazabuka, a rail-link between Livingstone and Victoria Falls in the south and Ndola in the north—the two identical spots cited by the dealer. In a booklet about the wildlife of the area he saw a photograph of an unusual skin, locally collected. The legend underneath described it as a pelt of the little known King Cheetah.

The 'lost' Messina King Cheetah skin. Lena and Paul Bottriell with owner Mr Jan Jourbert.

We were quick to learn that locating the Messina skin was only half the battle. The actual pelage revealed a brittleness that showed every sign of making examination of the skull difficult. If a cured and mounted pelt is in excellent condition with little sign of wear then a skull may be removed with care by an experienced taxidermist. Alas, in the case of the Messina specimen these conditions hardly applied. Forty years of exposure, in a hot climate, to dust and sunlight, not to mention the human touch, had resulted in the skin becoming thin and fragile, especially where it had been stretched over the skull. Consequently any attempt to separate the two was bedevilled by the very real possibility of the skin coming away in pieces, thereby virtually destroying a much-prized trophy that, in the eyes of its owner, was priceless. If the skin had belonged to us, needless to say, we wouldn't have hesitated to take the chance. But in any biological quest one must not for a moment arrogantly assume any rights in the name of research, or that the flame of enthusiasm that burns in one's own heart burns with the same intensity in the hearts of others.

There was one other avenue open to us: X-ray. Having a portable unit with us, we foresaw no problems. Time's preserving influence was to decree otherwise.

From the Shadows

"I have never had such a magnificent sight of wildlife as that presented by ... *Acinonyx rex*. I consider the male a more handsome animal than 'the Leopard, tiger or Lion...' "
John Buckmaster to Major A. L. Cooper, 14 July 1928

The discovery of a King Cheetah skull in the mounted head of a pelt, itself inexplicably "lost" to research for the best part of forty years, underlined to what extent the unexpected provides piquancy to the spice of quest. A subtle change of direction in conversation, with the aim of drawing Ivy out on the question of the provenances of his three King Cheetah skins, had paid dividends in several ways. The quality of the resultant X-rays, however, was mixed, due mostly to there being not one set but two. In addition to those taken by Paul and I on the portable unit, we had arranged through the good offices of Witwatersrand University for a separate set to be taken on a termograph, as back-up, at Johannesburg's Cancer Research Unit.

Initially, we hadn't been entirely happy with the products of our own efforts. Though readable, they lacked overall crispness, the outline of the skull being slightly fuzzed in parts. The X-ray intensity of the termograph, on the other hand, was such that with even the taxidermist's trademark tacks and pins standing out like Lowry figures, the white china clay, or kaolin as it is otherwise known, which had been packed and moulded round the skull to shape and fill out the mounted head instead of the more commonly used plaster of Paris had, after forty years, been transformed into a chunk of gleaming white porcelain which under the X-ray reflected as brightly as a polished mirror! Naturally this irreparably distorted the image. Fortunately the portable's X-ray photos were more satisfactory. Assisted by the Wits Dental Faculty we had plaster moulds made of the upper and lower jaws.

Subsequent examination of these along with the X-rays at the

The author X-raying in the field the mounted head
of the Messina skin containing the first authentic
King Cheetah skull to be traced.

Mammal Research Institute, with results confirmed by Smithers, revealed no significant cranial variation between the Messina skull and the cheetah in general. This suggested aberration, a simple pattern variant of the pelage. Yet, as has often been noted in leopards, aberrations are generally little more than "one-off" deviations from the norm. Certainly they are not as dramatically different in either frequency of occurrence or markings in the leopard as they are in the King Cheetah. If the King Cheetah is considered to be no more than an aberration it would have to be called a "standard" aberration, in deference to the striking uniformity between all King Cheetah specimens available for examination. Interestingly enough, the cheetah's skull is subject to variation. Very recent research has confirmed that cheetahs have a remarkably high level of morphological variation, or "fluctuating asymmetry", in their skulls (O'Brien et al., 1986). In other words in the general shape of a cheetah skull, features normally equal in size, such as the bones of the left and right side, can vary noticeably in any given individual.

It was at the Institute that a colleague of Smithers suggested we set in motion a reward scheme—a couple of thousand "bucks" to the person who led us to a live King Cheetah! Well, this was a notion calculated to raise passions. Certainly it had its dark side. Uppermost in our minds was the tragic disappearance of "Phuma", the last of the Timbavati white lions to live out its days in the wild. No sooner had these unique cats made headline news around the world than a bounty was put on their heads as offers running to five figures for the skin of one began to flood into southern Africa. Consequently, two of them, "Temba" and "Tombi", were transferred into the "protective custody" of Pretoria Zoo. It was already too late for "Phuma".

Approximately six weeks after she disappeared, Paul and I had one of those cheerless experiences you recall in flawless clarity long after the event. In our continuing search not only for live cheetahs but also for skins that might show the beginnings of a stripe or a blotch in their pattern, we found ourselves, one wet afternoon, nosing round the musty basement of a nefarious skin trader's establishment. The place was dim, lit only by paraffin lamps dotted haphazardly here and there. At one end a man in a brimmed hat pulled low about his ears talked in hushed tones to the trader as a bevy of Africans silently packed armloads of skins; the still, stale atmosphere reeked of naphthalene. We picked our way around the store, elephant tusks glinting in the half-light. From out of the gloom a face suddenly loomed up in front of us and a voice blurted out breathlessly, "do you want to buy a white lion skin?"

A furtive, stocky individual with fleshy, sweaty features otherwise unnotable, we stared back at him, our mouths agape. Our expres-

163

sions must have said it all, for within seconds he'd spirited himself away, leaving us standing blindly peering after him into the gloom like helpless, impotent fools. There was nothing we, nor anyone, could do. No official law protected animals as unique and beautiful as the white lions, although they had captured the imagination of the world for years. This well illustrated the dangers of a reward scheme. Soon, however, time would prevent us giving it another moment's thought, so much were events about to run away with us.

The official lack of attention paid to the King Cheetah sighting in Kruger Park, close to the Mozambique border in 1974 (not more recently, as at first suggested) still perplexed us, because it had been photographed—the first photograph of a live King Cheetah ever to be made known! The general consensus among Park management was that it may have strayed off through the Lebombos, out of Kruger, into Mozambique at some stage before the fence between the two countries had been completed later in the same year, 1974. In its opinion this barricade, built along a National boundary line suffering from guerilla activity, more than likely prevented the cat returning. Alternatively, it was argued, the cat may have perished, an assumption based on the average life expectancy of cheetahs in the wild. Another factor that probably had an inhibiting effect on its attitude to the sighting was its unanimous opinion that the King Cheetah was only an interesting aberration.

One day, not long after our minor scientific scoop with the skull, a colour feature article was published in a popular magazine and we got in touch for the first time with the tourist responsible for photographing the King Cheetah in Kruger Park. We learnt something we could scarcely believe. Not only did he have photographs, he had film, a couple of hundred feet of it, which the authorities of Kruger Park had tended to ignore. During the mildly mannered month of June, Ossie Schoof, a businessman from East London, had taken his family north on their annual pilgrimage to Kruger National Park. As far as his teenage son Gary was concerned they could go on doing so forever. With a tireless record of visits behind

164

them, the Schoofs had an enthusiasm to match and, consequently, they probably knew their animals and Kruger Park better than most tourists. On the morning of the sighting, while the remainder of the family slept, Ossie Schoof and his son Gary slipped out of their Rest camp in the south-central district around 6.30 and headed east. A short while later, further south on an untarred tourist road about 6 kilometres from the Mozambique border, Ossie brought the car to a sudden halt; a movement less than 100 metres off into the veld had caught his attention. Peering through the binoculars he was pleased to discover a small party of cheetahs in amongst the long, grass, frolicking unconcernedly. Downwind of the cats, which appeared to be on a progressively steady tack towards them, Schoof carefully positioned the cine camera on the window sill of the car and began to film while Gary prepared to take some still photos when the moment was right. As the cats, three in all, reached the road they lingered a moment at the edge before nonchalantly strolling across it directly in front of them. Father and son both knew they had captured something very special on film.

Ossie Schoof's good quality footage revealed a King Cheetah in prime condition, a magnificent young male apparently between ten and fifteen months old. Seeing the film for the first time, we were struck by the way the distinctive black and cream markings of the King Cheetah stood out alongside the sandy, spotted coats of the two ordinary cheetahs accompanying it, in this case its mother and sister. The mother was exceptionally handsome and strong-looking and noticeably larger than usual. We couldn't help thinking she could have taken on a leopard! She sharply rebuffed the young—though not so small—King Cheetah's sexual overtures during the filmed sequence.

Naturally enough, the film greatly excited Paul and I, and Schoof kindly placed it at our disposal. In retrospect, it seems hard to believe that it could have remained virtually unknown for so long. When Schoof and his son rushed back to camp with news of their remarkable sighting the officials they reported it to were plainly scornful. Schoof was indignant. He was a regular visitor to the

Clips from the first recorded film footage of a King Cheetah in the wild. "Like a leopard walking with a cheetah" is a not unrealistic eye-witness description when one looks at the strip of footage showing a King Cheetah with a spotted cheetah, filmed in Kruger Park. The rear view illustrates the striped and ringed tail of the King Cheetah — a consistent feature unique to these animals.

166

Park and felt he knew his animals. A straight, no-nonsense individual, he hardly struck one as a romancer. It took him almost six months to convince them of its significance. Not so with us. Suffice to say that the sight of a living, breathing King Cheetah strolling across the screen in technicolour worked wonders for the enthusiasm of those people we showed it to. As a direct consequence of this film we once again began to think about how to get a search started in Kruger Park.

At that time the Schoof sighting was five years old, which was a drawback, but one aspect of it made a follow-up irresistible. It had occurred within 7 kilometres of the Mozambique border, in other words the Lebombo Mountains, thereby cross-referencing those reports from the last century of ''woolly'' cheetahs said to wander among the gorges and rocky ravines of the Lebombos, a 300-kilometre range extending almost the entire length of Kruger Park. Now, of course, it was the prevailing situation that had to be considered. According to the most recent reports from Park officials, there had been no word of any King Cheetah appearing in the reserve since the Schoof sighting. But recent historical events made us sceptical. It is not widely known, for instance, that white lions appeared in Kruger Park for decades before Timbavati and Chris McBride apparently first introduced them to the world. In truth, little heed was ever paid to reports coming even from Park rangers. Anyone who has seen a white lion in the bush will tell you it stands out like an ice-cream.

But the idea of a search in Kruger had its opponents. We were told in quarters whence we initially least expected discouragement that we would be bogged down by bureaucratic wranglings and red tape before we knew what had hit us. Whether or not it emanated from zoo, museum, university or government conservation department the cry was the same, ''They won't co-operate with *us*; how can you ever expect them to co-operate with *you*, two unimportant foreigners on a private mission?''. Fortunately we were not part of the establishment milieu, a fact we had often discovered was to our advantage. Just how much advantage time alone would tell.

From Crocodile River the Lebombos run north along the Mozambique border towards Zimbabwe's Gonarezhou reserve, the only place it was once claimed where King Cheetahs had ever occurred. The range is well endowed with forest and bush which blend to form a quilt of vegetation that, at the imposing Lebombo Gorge, fans out across Mozambique to the Indian Ocean and northwards and eastwards in the direction of Zimbabwe and Tuli respectively. The Lebombos were typically representative of the sort of environment we believed King Cheetahs favoured, linked by virtue of their "vegetation type" with areas of southern Africa where the cats had been sighted and skins had been obtained. In the north-eastern Transvaal westward of the Park lies Vendaland, one of South Africa's Homelands. It is mountainous country reminiscent of Lebombo, though rising in many places to as much as 2000 metres above sea level. In some of the highest and least accessible parts, where the terrain is rough and the vegetation thick forest and thorn bush, the Venda bury their chiefs whose spirits, so legend has it, live on in the crocodile, while cheetahs reputedly guard their graves.

We first heard the legend from a German naturalist who had visited Vendaland from time to time to catch full grown crocodiles for his breeding station, the ultimate aim of which was the reintroduction of offspring to the wild state. It was while chasing up rumours of a white crocodile, said to live among the waterways in the foothills of the mountains, that he had first heard about the legend. The crocodile was considered sacred; and it was taboo for a stranger to question such a belief. But the German was a sharp, irascible sort of chap and couldn't restrain himself from chiding them on at least one point—the very idea of cheetahs living in such an environment! Surely they meant leopards? No, that was not what they meant. Cheetahs had been guarding the graves of Venda chiefs for generations, they assured him, a little put out by their guest's derisive manner. Having been guilty of what almost amounted to a heresy, the German wisely left it at that.

By a remarkable coincidence, within days of learning about the legend, we received news from a Game scout who told us how he had seen a King Cheetah skin wrapped around—what he assumed to be—a chief in the main town of Sibasa in Vendaland when he lived there as a teenager. Shades of Des Varaday and Malawi?! We certainly had no reason to doubt the validity of his observation. The scout's assumption that the African man wearing the skin was a chief was reasonable; any skin of unusual quality or character is invariably coveted by the headman of a tribe for one simple reason—class, his and the skin's!

According to an anthropologist we spoke to (a most charming woman who after many years living with the Venda was ordained an honorary witchdoctor) their insistence that the cats were cheetahs was intriguing. She herself had heard Venda speak of "the cheetahs in the hills" and always with the profoundest conviction. Knowing them as she did she said there was no reason to doubt their word: if the Venda said cheetah lived in the hills, "then cheetah lived in the hills!" was her final judgement on the matter. Observations of this nature should not simply be put down to that "tendency to embroider" syndrome some are wont to attach to the African. Legends among native peoples do not evolve over many generations merely out of some cheerful willingness to please or excite the occasional visitor. So we were obviously anxious to visit Vendaland. But there was a snag.

Vendaland was coming up for independence at the year's end. It was not, we were assured, an ideal time to apply for entry permits. Nor was it prudent. As the lead up to any homeland's independence always proved, it was an edgy period for Pretoria and, as a result, all forms of travel into Venda had been severely restricted, especially foreign travel which would apply to us. Even with a few influential words in high places the indications were that we might be lucky to get clearance in a little under, say, six months. Six months. Fortunately, unlike governments, legends keep.

The Hair and the Unicorn

Apart from indicating a strong correlation with the ordinary cheetah perhaps the most lasting contribution of the skull analysis to our research was that it wetted our appetites for more conclusive and more challenging evidence. For a long time Paul and I had wondered what hair analysis might reveal. With each King Cheetah pelt we handled we were impressed by the soft richness of the pelage. Unlike the coarser quality of an ordinary cheetah's coat, which is generally reminiscent of a short-haired dog's, these were significantly silky-soft to the touch, reminding us somewhat of that sumptuous feeling so characteristic of the well-bred, well-fed domestic cat in peak condition.

We were musing on this one day with Smithers at the Mammal Research Institute, over the head of the Messina King Cheetah whose worn and thinning pelage was a notable exception to the rule. Hair analysis, he reminded us, was a relatively new area of scientific research with institutions in only about four countries in the world having achieved a meaningful degree of success with it to date. There was little helpful information he himself could otherwise offer on the subject outside of suggesting we all ask around about it. Two days later the Director of the Institute favoured us with a priceless snippet of information. By a lucky chance he knew of a woman at the Institute of Medical Research in Johannesburg who at that very moment was working for a doctorate in hair analysis which, in his estimation, could make her unique in southern Africa, if not in Africa as a whole.

Having already started on a study of Africa's Felidae family, the prospect of analysing King Cheetah hair and adding the results to her paper more than delighted Hilary Keogh. A petite, pretty woman displaying no trace of the research scientist's "musty lab" image, she foresaw no problems in using hair from cured pelts provided they were in top-class condition. Hair samples taken from

170

the neck, the dorsal region directly behind the shoulders, and the mid-belly, would, we were told, give her a plentiful supply to work on. The scale pattern on a hair is notoriously variable with wear, hence the importance of the skins being of top quality.

Thus, armed to the teeth with an array of tiny, seal-proof glass bottles, we collected the required samples from four separate skins. The hairs had to measure between 20 and 60 millimetres and had to include both guard hair and underfur. The microstructure of each hair had to be examined in cross-section and along the hair shaft, where scales form a pattern of identification reminiscent of a fingerprint. It was this pattern—known as the cuticular scale pattern—that represented the key part of the analysis. From here the results, photographed under the microscope, would be compared with both leopard and ordinary cheetah hair. No less than ten clear samples were required before a test could provide acceptable evidence. Hilary produced more than half that amount again in the King Cheetah analysis. She already had the relevant test results for leopard and ordinary cheetah but that didn't include any known aberrant forms, which we felt could make for some intriguing comparisons. Subsequently, samples of ginger leopard hair were obtained with, for good measure, a number plundered from a black leopard—no easy task I can assure you. Thus, if only out of sheer curiosity, we felt reasonably excited about the prospects, though it's fair to say none of us expected anything revolutionary to result.

With the experiment reckoned to take a good three weeks to a month to complete, it was merely a matter of sitting back meanwhile and calmly awaiting the outcome. Sitting back calmly was hardly how it turned out. We hadn't counted on the unexpected, which came in the shape of news from Namibia which quite bowled us over. In response to a radio account of the expedition broadcast the previous week in Namibia (South-West Africa), a farmer in the north of the country was claiming to have shot and killed, in that same week, a King Cheetah. At a loss at first to know what he had shot, the account broadcast a few days later on the Afrikaans network, conveniently describing the King Cheetah and the expedi-

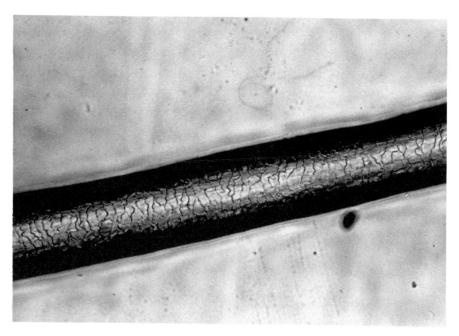

Microphotograph of sample ordinary cheetah *Acinonyx jubatus* hair showing "mosaic" cuticular scale pattern

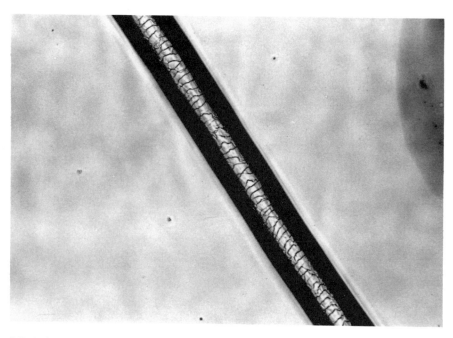

Microphotograph of sample King Cheetah *Acinonyx rex* hair showing "petal" cuticular scale pattern — corresponding, not to common cheetah, but leopard

172

tion's efforts to date, supplied the answer he'd been looking for. We have never regarded Namibia as likely King Cheetah country. It has the wrong vegetation type for a start; it is too desolate and too dry. And from the time of the earliest references to the King Cheetah, no sightings or skins have ever been recorded from here. A King Cheetah in Namibia defied all reason.

Was it then a "king-sized" cheetah the man had shot? Or a serval perhaps? We seemed to have travelled this path before. Despite these reservations, the farmer's claim demanded special attention. Firstly, the man was adamant it was not a "king-sized" cheetah he had shot; nor was it a serval (the tierboskat, or "tiger cat" as the Afrikaner calls it). Indeed, he went so far as to insist that it was a "young King Cheetah", one not fully grown which raised doubts about his having confused it with a serval. Still he was adamant: it was a King Cheetah, "with the stripes down its back". No less than half a dozen times did we question and verify everything he had to say during long-distance trunk calls to Grootfontein, which is really no more than a collection of cattle properties in the far north-east of Namibia.

But that was not all. He still had the skin. In the week since he'd shot it, there had only been time enough to have it cured locally. This prompted Paul to ask him if there were any bloodclots remaining on the pelt. The farmer deliberated for what seemed ages, then he came straight back with confirmation that there were some as the pelt had only been roughly salted and left to dry in the sun. Moreover, he'd also kept the skull of the cat, so puzzled had he been over its identity. After all, as he said himself, he had "never seen anything quite like it before!". Within the week we were in Windhoek, teutonic-toned capital of Namibia.

About 350 kilometres north of Windhoek lies Grootfontein, close to Etosha National Park and its salt pan, "place of mirages" and one of the great parade grounds for flamingos which occur here in their tens of thousands. Opened to the public as late as 1958 this National Park occupies only a quarter of the area originally planned for it (which was about twice the size of Switzerland). The German colonists set Ethosha aside as a game "preserve" way back in 1907. Covering a total of 22,270 square kilometres it remains one of the finest and largest of the world's reserves, boasting an extraordinary concentration of wildlife. The elephants here, perhaps two and a half thousand of them, are believed to be the tallest in Africa; the lions, some five hundred strong, are amongst the heaviest; and the rapier-horned gemsbok, known as the unicorn antelope because in profile its horns are so nearly parallel they seem as one, is so famous it is virtually Etosha's emblem.

With the entire 5000-kilometre trip there and back generously sponsored by *Scope Magazine* and Namib Airways, we flew the last leg of the journey to Grootfontein in, appropriately enough, an aircraft which virtually opened up Africa: a Dakota. We coasted along for about forty minutes on the final approach to Grootfontein at what seemed little more than 30 metres above ground. This precaution against being spotted by terrorists was hard on the nerves. The flat terrain, thick with thorn scrub that allowed a veteran craft the size of a Dakota to fly so low for so long, made a stark contrast to much of what we had seen previously of Namibia further south and west. Out of Windhoek the bronzed, ochry landscape with its gentle undulations was uncannily familiar. Like a gigantic, throbbing fossil the country had about it a pensive, inspiring presence, a soulful air that appealed to my spirit and rekindled my love of desertscape which had been shaped already by my own vast, baroque-painted southern land, Australia.

Windhoek for its part is a warm, open town with a singular charm evident in its old German-style buildings and friendly beer-gardens, as well as its stately Hereros women who grace its streets in flowing patchwork gowns that are both a proud symbol of group identity and marvels of colour. By contrast, the ironically named Grootfontein, meaning ''great fountain'', is the archetypal small puddle marked by little more than an airstrip and an all-purpose store. Its small country-community mood is overshadowed somewhat by a big fish in the shape of a military base that lies rambling and quiet in the heat haze like some great, fat puff adder ready to strike at the merest whisper of a threat. Quietly tolerated by the locals because of the reality of the time and place they lived in— their homesteads were surrounded by three-metre-high, heavy-duty wire fencing— the joie de vivre of the farming community still showed through despite the grim presence. On the very eve of our departure, in fact, guerillas had made a dramatic incursion south out of Angola to within 30 kilometres of Grootfontein, attacking a number of remote farms with deadly effect. We were at the airport at the time, waiting to board our flight, when this news broke. Apart from a short delay of some ten minutes, it seemed to be of little concern to our fellow passengers. Here, as elsewhere in Africa, life had to go on.

Indeed, Namibia was reasonably peaceful at that time, with the people we met as broad and as open as the country itself. One dear lady, the only other passenger on the flight north out of Windhoek, invited us to lunch as soon as we made her acquaintance. The fact that we were heading in the same direction was a good enough reason for her. After what had been a most harrowing last hour of flight, literally ''bouncing'' our way along—that being the nature of low altitude flight and Dakotas—cheek by jowl with the ground, her attractive invitation was impossible to refuse.

''It's not a King Cheetah!'' The words fell like bricks as Paul uttered them. Jos Van Zyl had been pent up for days with excitement over our visit; apart from the skin, he had a fund of things to talk about and show us. Indeed, at first, this youthful family man who was unreservedly enthusiastic about everything, and who bit chunks out of the English language, actually appeared to have lost all notion of why we were there. Not till Paul, unable to bear the suspense any longer, gently prodded him about the King Cheetah, did he stop short, clearly aghast at his own laxity. He whacked his forehead soundly with the heel of his hand and immediately whisked us off, to the accompaniment of a torrent of apologies and embarrassed chatter, to a large room in the homestead where, alluringly draped over the back of an armchair, was the striped skin we'd just travelled two and a half thousand kilometres to see.

There was no mistaking it... and I felt myself go cold all over. Only Paul's voice cutting through a sudden icy silence like a chainsaw, told me my eyes weren't play-acting. Two and a half thousand kilometres! For nothing! He had killed a serval, but Jos Van Zyl genuinely didn't know it. Merely being born in Africa doesn't presuppose a wide or expert knowledge of her wildlife. Like so much else, it has to be learnt. A substantial number of people in the sub-continent haven't even seen a wild elephant, or would know what a serval, or a caracal for that matter, might look like. In these days of increased public awareness of the world's wildlife any of the major zoos in Europe or North America may still ring with misinformed cries of, "Oh look! A tiger" when it is actually a leopard. So too can visitors to rival establishments in Pretoria or Johannesburg be heard to drop clangers of equal magnitude. As even the most expert among us are at some stage, Jos was a greenhorn in such matters. Following a lifelong career as a mines engineer he had, after all, been farming "out in the sticks" for only two short years.

In general, his attitude to wildlife was little different to that of many of the white farmers in neighbouring South Africa. Like them, he prided himself on his ability to use a gun. A perfect example of this is the story he told about the night he shot two spotted cheetahs from his vehicle while driving to a neighbouring property for dinner. The animals were standing together by the roadside when he sighted them. Though his stock had never been troubled by cheetahs, without thinking, he grabbed for his rifle and fired a couple of quick shots through the window. To his surprise, the pair staggered off into the bush behind, indicating he had hit them both. But not having his shooting lamp or even a torch with him, he didn't follow after them there and then. Instead he returned some hours later with a light. Just a few metres in from the road, amongst some long grass, he found them both dead. In his own words they were "lying side by side, their soft heads touching and their legs seemingly around each other". Even pragmatic Jos was moved by the sight. But, as he then lifted up, with gleeful, boyish pride, the handsome, well cured pelt of one of the cheetahs in

176

question, one realised that he had not been moved for long. As it would have been churlish of us to have started lecturing our host on the immorality, the inefficiency—call it what you like—of shooting every four-legged beast that moves simply for the sake of it, we urged him to be a little more discriminating. If, as we pointed out, he went on haphazardly pot-shotting animals, whether they were a threat to his livelihood or not, especially servals and the smaller carnivores—among them caracals, wild cats, civets and genets—he could and would give himself a real head-ache because of the resulting increase in vermin. He would be removing the one sure control, given freely to him by nature, that the farmer has over the rodent population. Indeed it is this, the simple, raw economics of life—rather than the tragically under-valued argument that in a world of humans and animals, each is necessary for the continued well-being and wholeness of the other—that the farmer of Africa, like the tribal African, appreciates.

Despite our disappointment, taking our leave of Namibia was painful. Our stay with the Van Zyls in their haunting, sunburnt country was like one long feast for body and soul; a plentiful supply of sunshine, wine and spirited, friendly people, topped up with sumptuous cooking, in a sumptuous amber-soaked environment was just the aperitif we had needed.

When we saw Hilary Keogh again on our return to South Africa she had some astonishing news for us. Her analysis of the hair samples Paul and I had collected had shown a fundamental distinction between King Cheetah and ordinary cheetah. With cuticular scaling on a hairshaft, it is invariably towards the base of an individual hair—where it receives most of its protein and where, as a result, the scale pattern is at its most distinctive—that irregularities will show. In the microstructure of the hair samples Hilary had studied her examination revealed that in the cuticular scale pattern on the guard hair of *Acinonyx jubatus*, that is to say the ordinary cheetah, the pattern was clearly mosaic, meaning that the scales or lines run across the hairshaft in a haphazard fashion, just like a mosaic. Now, on the King Cheetah guard hair—remembering that the

177

animal we are talking about is still a cheetah, or at least a cheetah "type"—the scaling was unmistakeably petal, especially towards the base, which is to say that the lines or scales lay across the hair-shaft in a regular and more orderly pattern of leaves or "petals". This petal pattern is a feature of leopard guard hair!

This revelation certainly sent a few interested parties reeling, ourselves not the least among them. One inevitable result of all this was that the argument for the King Cheetah being a hybrid immediately reasserted itself. This argument had originally found favour in some quarters purely on the basis of the size of King Cheetah skins which indicated a bigger cat than the ordinary cheetah, its legs thicker set and comparable to those of the leopard. We had never held with the hybrid theory which, in the King's case, was a supposed cheetah/leopard combination. Apart from appreciating that a leopard will kill an ordinary cheetah given the opportunity (the other way around is inconceivable), the King Cheetah—size, markings, length of fur, mane, etc. aside—retains features too obviously resembling those of the ordinary spotted cheetah, namely the partially non-retractile claws, the characteristic facial "tear marks" running from the eye to the upper lip, and the similar skull and teeth structure (as indicated by the Messina X-rays). In short, it has a general cheetah-like appearance.

What most concerned us, however, was the question of how a cat like the King Cheetah could pass on an attribute of another cat belonging to a completely different species and genus. The additional premise that the King Cheetah was, for instance, an aberration, only complicated the issue. Subsequently it was suggested that the King Cheetah may equally have resulted from a cross between a cheetah and a leopard as from a single mutation. The crossing hypothesis could be explained in this way: a young male leopard encounters a fully grown female cheetah in oestrus, that is to say on heat. They mate—if the situation was reversed a female leopard would tear a cheetah's throat out instead—then go their separate ways. If there are any offspring, those more cheetah-like in character will naturally be better able to keep up with a cheetah

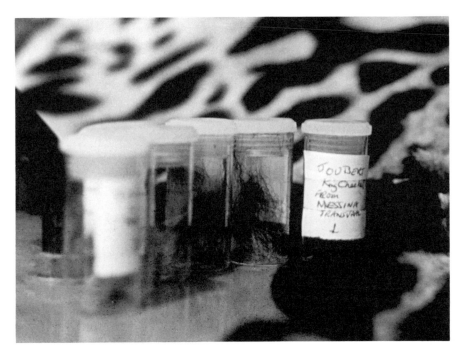

Specimens of King Cheetah hair.

mother, more able to live and hunt as a cheetah and thus would be better equipped for survival.

At the same time, might it not also be possible that way back in the remote past cheetah and leopard were one and the same? Possible, but hardly probable. It is believed that the cheetah evolved quite independently from the other big cats, namely the *Panthera* group (lion, leopard, tiger etc.), which are distinguished from the cheetah by the presence of a hyoid bone in the throat which permits them to roar. Biochemical evidence, however, suggests that the bigger cats are all very closely related, with individual origins (when some sort of adaptive differentiation took place between them) probably dating no further back than the early- to mid-Pliocene era, roughly between four and twelve million years ago. Recent studies have demonstrated that cheetahs display notably low levels of genetic variation due, it is believed, to population bottlenecks resulting in inbreeding. Possibly these bottlenecks have been caused in recent times by intensive poaching and in the

179

ancient past by severe ecological upheavals, such as occurred in the late-Pleistocene era when many big, specialised carnivores became extinct. Such a paucity of genetic variation makes the dramatic presence of the King Cheetah all the more intriguing. On another level, it certainly confirms why variants of the modern cheetah—in striking contrast to all the other cats—have always been so rare. At yet another level, there may be a connection between the leopard attribute in the hair of the King Cheetah, as demonstrated by the hair analysis, and atavism (a tendency to reproduce ancestral rather than parental characters, the result being what is popularly known as a throwback). It is said that many felines have derived their spotted markings from a "primitive" striped coat, the stripes having gradually broken up into a lighter, more diffused pattern of spotting as the animals moved out of jungle and other heavily forested environments with the spread of more open grassland areas. It is conceivable, then, that the King Cheetah pattern of today, as a recessive form, is a throwback to a forest-dwelling ancestor. This could make it the original pattern of the first cheetah to have evolved (a similar explanation has been proposed for the reticulated giraffe). This pattern later gave way, for adaptive reasons, to the spotted coat of the ordinary cheetah. But if this is the case, then surely cheetahs like the King should have appeared sporadically among the previously large populations of cheetah which inhabited parts of East and North Africa and Asia during the thousands of years man and cheetah have associated?

If, on the other hand, the King Cheetah has only arisen recently as the result of a local mutation, the frequency and consistency of the King Cheetah pattern in known specimens this century may be accounted for by the gradual emergence of a new race of cheetah. Unfortunately, severe reductions in wildlife habitat and the indiscriminate slaughter of cheetahs could have interrupted the process to an extent we will never be able to judge. There was no tidy scientific answer to the results of the hair analysis. Perhaps only controlled research using living animals would solve the riddle. A vet on behalf of a certain zoo even mooted the offer of a plot of land being made available for breeding purposes if and when we located King Cheetahs alive in the wild. Whatever the outcome of that, we began to seriously consider that even without live King Cheetahs, selective breeding using common spotted cheetah from those areas where King Cheetah have been recorded, could, in the end, be the answer. After all, this is how man has developed special breeds of cattle, dogs, horses and sheep.

Operation Zebra Pen

Generally speaking, the rules governing the movement of visitors in and around Game reserves are strict, for obvious reasons. Certainly, when out game-viewing in Kruger Park, people are obliged to keep to their vehicles, to use only designated tourist roads, and to restrict their times of travel to the daylight hours. Consequently, we could not have guessed that, from one television interview, an invitation to carry out a major search in Kruger Park would be extended to us. Our expedition enjoyed a good relationship with the media. In addition to mildly exotic events, such as Paul and I appearing as ourselves alongside "visitors" from outer space in search of the King Cheetah in a children's Sci-fi television series filmed at Eric and Janet Nordh's Cheetah Park, Yorkshire Television were to pursue us across Africa on behalf of Arthur C. Clarke for a more up-market series that has since turned into a best-seller. It led to some valuable revelations too; among them a final, illuminating answer to the mysterious "Lobatse skin".

Officially listed for years as a full jacket made up from a single, flat King Cheetah skin, it had always seemed inconceivable that this could have been made from just one pelt. Proper investigation showed that the doubts were justified. The supposed single King Cheetah pelt was, in fact, a concoction of three or more serval pelts, which an extant photograph of the jacket clearly shows. Made up into a coat by a Johannesburg furrier from skins collected by a skin trader in Botswana, it had later been worn by the man's daughter into the office of a renowned feature writer on one of Africa's major daily newspapers. The furrier, an astute man, still believes the coat is that of a King Cheetah. Described as "probably the most singular fur coat in the world", he confesses to thinking it was "hideous in the extreme" at the time. Its eventual owner obviously thought so too, for it went "missing" in bizarre cir-

Paul and Lena Bottriell discussing operations with Kruger Park Senior Game Ranger, Ted Whitfield.

cumstances in London after she threw it at her flatmate in a fit of pique. We still have our photograph of it.

The launch of a reward scheme in *Scope* proved to be a lame duck. Not so the television chat show that followed directly after, on SATV. We were billed to share the platform with a tame cheetah and a ''surprise'' guest. He was a surprise alright; the repercussions of that single half-hour billing was pure soap opera. A vet in the service of Kruger Park's arch rival, the Department of Nature Conservation, he'd once incensed that compelling maverick Chris McBride in front of the same viewing public with the wild and essentially incorrect charge that the white lions McBride had made famous round the world were ''frauds'', were nothing more than albinos. It was a mischievous charge for which the sardonic, combustible McBride extracted both an embarrassed apology and a retraction from the Department of Nature Conservation. This same contentious vet, in the closing minutes of the programme with us, dropped a massive clanger which may still be reverberating in certain quarters, about how some years back in

183

Kruger Park, while carrying out an independent survey for his department, he had seen a King Cheetah but had declined, so he says, to report it to official sources either at the Park or his department on the grounds that he had no intention of divulging its whereabouts. This gave us a golden opportunity, which we acted upon swiftly.

Within forty-eight hours, at National Parks HQ in Pretoria, the Chairman and his Director, clearly irritated by what had transpired on their television screens two nights previously, were cordially inviting Paul and I to carry out a study of our own in Kruger Park—the search the cynics reckoned would never be allowed—without any of the basic restrictions that applied to tourists. Our chat-show colleague had done us a favour beyond our, and I daresay his, wildest imaginings.

By lifting restrictions we were automatically given as much freedom as any park official; all that was expected of us was that we should not abuse the rights and privileges accorded us. Spoilt as we had been by the freedom of the wild open bush where no official rules as such exist to govern one's movements, it was still an opportunity not to be underestimated. During the early days of our research, long before embarking for Africa with the expedition, we had come across a vivid reference to the Messina King Cheetah in a set of old *African Wild Life* magazines Paul had carried around with him from country to country, along with other sacrosanct memorabilia. It was in one of the 1962 issues that there appeared a short commentary from a member of the Transvaal Museum in which he said that, without doubt, the King Cheetah was also an inhabitant of the northern Transvaal, citing as evidence not only the Kongo farm specimen, but also claims of King Cheetahs having been seen from time to time in Kruger Park.

To bring matters right up to date, the Schoof sighting, as was becoming more obvious all the time, was only one of a number in Kruger Park to be backed up by photographic evidence. The second report, received through a press contact of a Pretoria man, revealed portrait shots of exceptional quality of the very same King

184

Cheetah some three years later! Learning to recognise from photographs individual animals belonging to a patterned race is relatively easy because no two striped, blotched or spotted animals from the same species have identical patterns. Each ocelot, giraffe or King Cheetah is unique; a zebra foal will even recognise its mother by her stripes. Thus, in its way, the markings of an individual patterned animal constitute its "fingerprint", its personal ID if you like.

We made plans to concentrate what turned out to be a preliminary search in the South Central District where both sightings had occurred. The second sighting had also occurred in the winter, near Satara rest camp, roughly 30 kilometres as the crow flies from the area where the Schoofs had filmed and photographed the same King Cheetah nearly three years previously. Incredibly, through a potential sponsor, we were to uncover yet another sighting of the same King Cheetah. This time it had been observed and photographed at a later date, reputedly in early 1978, close to a place called Nwanedzi which nestles far into the foothills of the Lebombos. The site forms the apex of a triangle linking the previous two photographed sightings, defining an area either kept to or returned to by the cat in question on at least three occasions in four years. Little credence was given to the vet's claim. Perhaps he had seen a King Cheetah, perhaps not. We had no means of telling. Finally, with fuel and food sponsorship organised, we were on our way; naturally, "accommodation" in the Park, for want of a better word, would be free. The only luxury donations we allowed ourselves were the loan of a 16 mm cine camera and the gift of a crate of the best wine for those blissful nights to come under Southern Cross skies.

Though the name itself may not conjure up romantic images, our stay in the "Zebra Pen" will forever remain one of my happiest memories of Africa. For sheer novelty it came close to eclipsing the camp at Tuli, although with all due respect to Kruger Park, camping out in the reserve could never compare with that Eden on the Limpopo. There Paul and I could wander naked if we chose and never be bothered by convention. Living in the untamed bush at

185

Tuli was the closest I've ever come to sublime contentment, for the wild is a powerful aphrodisiac as well as a cure for all the mundanity and trauma of the nine-to-five world.

The Zebra Pen had atmosphere. It was, quite simply, a kind of stockade for game covering perhaps half an acre, maybe less, completely enclosed by a high, wooden palisade. Surrounding a wide court-yard, three sides were fenced off from stables with the remaining one roofed over by a flat, corrugated-iron awning of a width adequate for the protection of our stores and equipment. Not used for years, the Pen at one time had housed zebra for inoculation purposes. Now its only regular inhabitants were dwarf mongooses, snakes, and a variety of rather hirsute arachnids!

We did find two quite unexpected luxuries there. A makeshift, brush-fence shower, made private—more for reasons of protection than for modesty—by a fence made of thin bamboo reeds lashed together to form a circular cubicle open to the sky, within which was a couple of rocks, smoothed flat and shoved together to serve as a floor. A cold water shower, early-morning-invigorating and bliss at high noon, worked off the Park's water supply. The lack of a door, or baffle, was its only drawback; the slightest breeze creeping in through that opening off a draughty courtyard during late afternoon, when the heat of the sun had almost gone, made the simple task of washing away the dust and sweat which pastes the body like a second skin after a day's bushslogging resemble the Chinese water torture!

The other luxury was a long-drop of the wrap-around, grass-walled, gallon-drum variety set into the top of a hole in the ground and situated at a healthy distance from the Pen. A luxury because it had already been dug and constructed, it was sophisticated as long-drops go. Most certainly, however, it was not of the type one should linger in, for snakes, too, have a penchant for lingering—though for somewhat different reasons—in the cosier bush latrines.

The story of an encounter I had with a snake in the Pen was unnerving enough to warrant re-telling here. Tripping nimble-footed across to the shower one morning draped only in a skimpy towel, I was brought skidding to a standstill by the sudden, mindrivetting sight at eye-level of a snake in the shower entrance, just two feet away coiled round some loose sticks of bamboo and spitting menacingly in my direction. I was lucky to see it! The bamboo, dried and yellowish, offered perfect camouflage for the snake's markings which I clearly remember thinking, before I threw my towel at it, were remarkably intricate in pattern and colour. It is extraordinary how in situations of this sort, one's senses record sights and sounds with such microscopic attention to detail. Though not immediately recognisable as a particularly toxic type, no one takes chances with snakes; especially in my state of undress! Seeing my dust, Pul was there in a flash with our trusty broom to deal with the snake "long-distance style"—the one good reason, he always insisted, why no expedition should ever be without one! In the centre of the Pen's courtyard, rising like some majestic high altar, we made our campfire, always an integral part of our universe. About three feet in diameter and built up with dozens of logs the thickness and length of a man's leg, it roared up almost the instant it was set alight, mellowing as evening passed to a rich smoulder, enough to boil a kettle or cook a meal; a gentle daily kindle and an occasional top-up with the odd log or two provented it from ever burning out the whole time we were there. Some evenings that great fire would become an almost supernal well of comfort as from under a ripe, round hunter's-moon, primal choruses of hyenas would come probing and groping through the shadows like the chill fingers of fate. For those who've experienced it, Africa offers no more ominous call than the whoop, whoop, whhooo-upp of hyenas gathering at the kill, a mad, gut-turning sound exhorting all to remember what could await them.

With the onset of the Lowveld winter the night temperatures, too, were turning increasingly chilly after the still-searing heat of day. As a result, we frequently took to sleeping in the back of the one landrover we'd brought with us, "Ingwe", specially fitted out for this purpose. It was a cosy set-up, sometimes too cosy, a situation doubtless abetted by the fact that we always parked her at night well in from the main gate to the Pen, close to the courtyard where the high fences of the stockade and sundry adjoining stables and sheds afforded a degree of protection from the sharp night air. Thus, on warmer evenings we simply didn't bother and slept under the stars. Lying there, our heads close to the ground, the earth would come alive beneath us with the drumming of hooves shivering through the land and catching in the rocks and trees the closer it came, a wild, wilful wave of sound as compelling to the senses as music.

Often, too, a small herd of elephants would circumnavigate the Pen, hugging close to the perimeter fence. As soft of tread as elephants are, they can be awkward, even noisy, in the small hours in a game park such as Kruger where they have little need to be on their guard. In the dead of night the acoustical properties of the Zebra Pen transmitted sounds so well that those huge pachyderms seemed much too close for comfort, the apparent snug confines of the Pen offering little reassurance if one paused to think that any one of them could have knocked a way through those palisades as though they were just so many matchsticks!

The Zebra Pen is situated in the South Central District of Kruger Park near Tshokwane, home base for the area game ranger, our only "neighbour" and rarely seen in the course of a day. Paul and I concentrated our efforts over roughly a 1400-square-kilometre patch of country which formed a rectangle stretching north from Tshokwane to Satara and across from Minsane Mond waterhole in the east, to the Mozambique border and the Lebombos. This area encompassed the spots where the three sightings of King Cheetah had been verified.

Although normal restrictions governing the movement of tourists did not rigidly apply to us, we were nonetheless expected to avoid travelling through the reserve at night if possible. Working at night in a major game park is very different from operating night recces in the freer atmosphere of the open bush as we had done in Tuli. In the closed confines of a reserve, no matter how large, one feels much like a marauder plunging through the silent dark, an unwarranted nuisance to the animal inhabitants whose only respite from a day filled with the smells and sounds of hundreds, nay thousands of ogling human beings, is the sweet, secretive seclusion of the African night.

Joseph, Tshokwane area Game Scout, seconded to first search.

As an aid in getting to know the lay of the part of the Park we'd be working, we were assigned a game scout, a Shangaan from Mozambique by name of Joseph who told us in Fanagalo of the times as a boy he had heard elders speak of the striped cheetahs "in the hills", the Lebombos, where sometimes the tribe would go to hunt. (His particular reference to the Lebombos indicated something more than just a fond wish to please). Certain tracts of land clearly supported a greater biomass than others; and naturally enough, where game moved in large numbers, so did the predators. Some areas had a definite lure for vast herds of the same type of animal, such as the large plain where we always came across a magnificent herd of buffalos, usually two to three hundred strong, grazing with almost no other species in sight.

Further east, from Nwanedzi down along the Lebombos, the terrain became hillier and more undulating and the vegetation denser as we moved closer the border. In this strip of the reserve we noticed giraffe with distinctly heavier colouring, though the fragmentary pattern typical of the southern sub-species was still

189

evident. A supposed symptom of advancing age, some specimens were reminiscent of the reticulated giraffe of Uganda and Kenya. There is a theory that the colouring of the giraffe when young, in all races in Africa, really is that of the reticulated variety in which the blotches of the giraffe's pattern appear much larger and more regularly polygonal, separated by a pale cream network of expressly narrow lines. As the pattern in these cases of young giraffe is rated as being more ''primitive'', the inference is that the reticulate colouring is the giraffe's original, from which all others have evolved. It is a theory with striking parallels.

It was in Kruger that I saw wild sable antelope for the first time. Magnificent warrior game animals with such a distinguished air about them, they are undoubtedly the noblest, yet fiercest antelope in Africa. Possibly even more strikingly beautiful than the roan, with a glossy, black-brown hide and bristling mane, crowned by a fine tapering head and rapier-sharp horns that will run a lion through in one sweep, the sable is one of Africa's greatest treasures and one which is always immediately recognisable. Though sensitive to changes in grazing areas there were reputed to be around 1100 sables in the Park at the time we were there and they are hopefully on the increase. Most other species are represented in reasonable numbers in the reserve and it was heartening to learn that low-ratio groups like the tsessebe and, more especially, the wild dog are on the increase. Heartening, too, was the news that there were believed to be nearly a thousand leopards in the reserve. But this was not surprising. A past master at concealment, the leopard's adaptability and sheer skill as a hunter has allowed it to survive the onslaught of predator man. The leopard is, indeed, the ultimate cat.

Gradually, we got to know the South Central District, its geography, where the game congregated mostly, and what we were likely to see on any given day in a particular area. We also added some breathtaking studies to our already vast stock of photographs. We also had some breathtaking encounters! Like the time we ended up hurtling backwards in ''Ingwe'' down a steep, dirt track at breakneck speed due to a bull elephant taking a sudden aversion to our presence. He kept up the charge for a good hundred metres or so; and just when at one treacherous-looking bend we thought he was about to have us, he sheered off back into the bush.

Of course, elephants aren't always so unpredictably aggressive as experience had taught me since first riding elephant-back in the foothills of the Himalayas in search of tigers. (There is no good evidence that the African elephant is more temperamental, ergo more dangerous, than the Asian). Impossible to forget is the occasion when we came across two elephants in a secluded corner of the bundu "consummating their troth", so to speak. When the bull's ardour had at last subsided he turned, staggered across to the nearest tree, and literally "plopping" his brow against it in what was a clear gesture of exhaustion, remained leaning there for a good twenty minutes or so feebly fanning himself with his two great ears! In describing elephants, no one has put it better than Daphne Sheldrick: "So huge, yet so vulnerable, so powerful yet so gentle... so vitally important to the ecology...".

We also got to know something of the people who live and work in Kruger, a vital factor in picking up worthwhile information on probable sightings. Though disparate in occupation, what they all had in common was an abundance of hospitality and a keen interest in our work. It was in just this way we heard about a member of staff in the village office at Satara rest camp who was reputed to have seen a cheetah remarkably like "ours" less than 18 months before, en route to the Gudzane Windmill, roughly twenty kilometres cross-country, north-west of Satara. It wasn't as if she had just off-handedly mentioned the incident to her colleagues; she had spoken of it at the time of the sighting. Certainly, the position of the sighting as she described it to us fitted in with the three verified ones, the Schoofs's, the one just south of Satara, and the one near Nwanedzi.

The game rangers were generally more guarded in their approach, although at the same time they were as curious as the next person to discover whether the King Cheetah was a true denizen of the Park or just a chance visitor. Base for Tom, one of the Park's youngest rangers, was Nwanedzi, a lonely yet picturesque post not

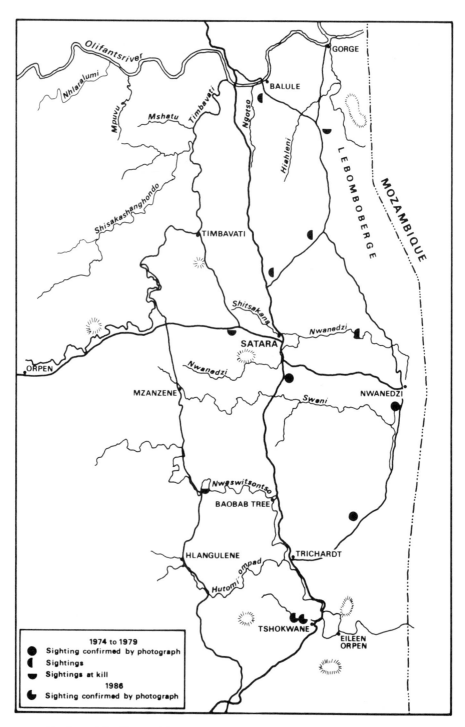

Section of the Kruger National Park showing sightings of King Cheetahs.

192

many miles in from the sensitive border with Mozambique and near to where a para-military unit operated. The unit's task was to maintain security in and around the border zone; and it was just south of here, in 1978, that the King Cheetah had been sighted and photographed for the third time. According to the ranger, a pilot flying with the only commercial airline operating at that time to and from Kruger maintained he'd seen at some time during the first few months of 1979, without any prior knowledge of the supposed sighting en route to Gudzane, "a big, heavily-marked cat", with some sort of stripes he thought, strolling nonchalantly along a firebreak where it crossed the tourist route to Mavumbye Reservoir and Gudzane itself.

Although only in his mid-twenties Tom had experienced excitement enough for a lifetime. Only a year or so earlier, for instance, he'd been attacked by a crocodile in the Nwanedzi River where he and a couple of colleagues had been repairing a dam wall. He told us he was submerged in water up to the waist (the stretch of water in question is not very deep) when a 14-15-foot-long crocodile struck, without warning, and dragged him under. Few of us realise how immense even a 12-foot croc is, let alone one of greater length. Standing probably some three feet off the ground and weighing in at around a ton, a crocodile of the size that hit the ranger would be truly a monster.

At the instant it hit him, Tom told us, there was a severe thud, and then nothing but searing pain as the croc's jaws engulfed his leg and pulled him down through the water, now a surging mass of foam. Within seconds he remembers an almost supernatural will to live taking hold of him and, with it, a realisation beyond the pain and horror that, if he was going to survive, he was going to have to fight. With chest and lungs heaving, he fumbled for his knife; he clutched the grip hard; then, with every ounce of strength he could muster, he wrenched his arm up and out of the water and began to lash out wildly at the giant saurian, thrusting the blade again and again into the creature's face and eyes in the desperate, prayerful hope that it would let go. Fortunately his mates, only a little way from the river, heard the commotion and rushed back to

193

his rescue. They were later publicly honoured for saving their colleague's life. Tom's leg was severely injured. Happily it healed sufficiently for him to walk again, a croc's jaws being designed for catching and holding rather than for "snapping" or cutting. He survived, doubtless gaining a degree of serenity as a result. A walk with death, after all, is a humbling event. Few have lived to tell a similar tale from personal experience.

Late one afternoon, shortly before sundown, we turned off along a firebreak. This one had a quaint familiarity about it; only a week before, along the same firebreak, we'd rounded a bend straight into a pride of lions spread across it. Elsewhere along its length the track hugged a watercourse across country, the vegetation on either side of it dipping between hollows and kopjes of riverine landscape and scrub. Then "it happened". Suddenly, we were no different to anyone else who has claimed to have spotted a King Cheetah. On the other side of the river stood an animal with long legs, erect head and lithe body. Through binoculars, in the strange light of late day, we both identified on that animal what we believed to be the markings of a King Cheetah. The blood drained into my boots.

We had permission to drive straight across the open bush in such an event, but the condition of the river bank wasn't at all conducive to a crossing, whichever side of the river we looked. Neither was there time to debate the matter. We tore off downstream in the hope of finding a way over. Apart from the likely chance of the cat spiriting itself away, the light was also against us, fading fast as it does, come late afternoon in the wild at the height of the dry, when even in photographs, whatever the lens, and whatever the distance, animals can come up looking little more than silhouettes. In addition we'd been assured by the Park authorities that they would activate an immediate aerial search of their own if we produced some photographic proof; without it the Warden couldn't justify a search. But what about us undertaking a search of our own? And if we did, what kind of transport should we use? Anything like the light plane the Park would have doubtless opted for, as they tend to in game counts, was out of the question. What we needed, as

194

Paul neatly put it, was something that would "float gently above the treetops". By the time we'd bade farewell to the Zebra Pen and were winding our way out of the Park through the lovely sloping country of its south-east corner, we'd been wonderfully inspired. Why not float over Kruger Park... in a balloon?

It had never been done before. In Pretoria, a good 350 kilometres away, we made a personal request to the Director of National Parks who in turn put it to the board. They decided in our favour and within ten days had given us the official go-ahead for the first balloon search ever to be undertaken in Kruger Park. Hot-air balloons operate on the very simple principle that heated air rises. With a gas burner suspended on a large steel frame above the rim of the basket, air heated by the burner fills the synthetic envelope, or balloon, attached overhead on cables, causing it to rise, taking the basket up with it. Of course there is an element of fire-risk where vast tracts of bushland are involved, especially in the dry. Consequently African Oxygen the sponsoring firm which laid on for our use the company's hot-air balloon complete with a team of pilots, all the propane gas required for the exercise, and a generous cash donation, also undertook to indemnify Kruger Park against the risk of fire damage in the course of setting up and operating the balloon, with the inclusion of fire extinguishers and fire-resistant blankets a necessary adjunct.

Apart from additional financial sponsorship from a variety of sources in the commercial sector, Avis, Coca-Cola, and Siemens among others, there were the offers of non-financial help that constitute almost the life-blood of an expedition. There were outright donations and loans of goods, such as extra tents and camping equipment from the Scouts to help cope with an expected influx of people (twelve at any given time). We received a 40-foot radio mast for the camp from an electronics firm, as well as several walkie-talkies powerful enough to communicate both with the airborne balloon from the ground and from vehicle to vehicle. A brand new Landcruiser, provided by Toyota, was to prove ideal, because of its nimbleness, for carting round the balloon, its basket, crew and tackle. And there were sundry other donations: colour and black-and-white film, heavy-duty batteries, cameras... and even a cheque for R10 which we found stuck under a windscreen wiper on one of the vehicles. It was the gift of a student at Wits University who, until then, had been no more to us than a face in the crowd.

One stipulation in the middle of all this planning and preparation gave us cause for alarm. Although DCA willingly granted us the necessary permission to fly over Kruger, we were cautioned by the military to avoid drifting too near to the Mozambique border—we were advised to ditch the craft if need be. In the eyes of guerilla snipers, we were told, a pretty little balloon like ours made an irresistible target.

Balloon over the Bushveld

The King Cheetah Balloon Search over Kruger Park was unique in several ways. But, like most original and ambitious enterprises, it could not—in the most literal sense—have got off the ground without the enthusiastic collaboration of a variety of helpers. With up to a dozen crew to accommodate and feed each day, our full team comprised a mixed-bag of people, from pilots and newspaper reporters to those whose only qualification for being there was that rare, altruistic kind of enthusiasm which benefits every expedition. There was big Willie du Plessis, a soft-spoken bear of a man from Canon cameras; an affable Englishman, Roger Newby, who had become keen on gliding and ballooning during a sojourn in Australia; young Gary Schoof, the first man to photograph the Kruger Park King Cheetah; Jan Hamman, Press Photographer of the Year and wildlife enthusiast. Even our daughters were there to help us, released for the long summer holidays from their convent boarding school in England, where they'd volunteered for temporary banishment from the free world nearly a year before. If nothing else, they ended up experts at inflating and retrieving hot-air balloons!

Embodying elements of fantasy and originality in equal measure, a balloon quest for a rare animal, with Africa the tantalising backdrop, was a publicity agent's dream. We had been in Africa eleven months and our search had taken us across the continent from Zimbabwe and the northern Transvaal, through Tuli in Botswana, to Namibia. This major search initiative was destined to be the closing gambit in the present fieldwork to locate one or more live King Cheetah in the wild. There remained the one alternative that was completely independent of locating King Cheetahs in the wild: selective breeding, using ordinary cheetahs from those areas of southern Africa ascertained from our research to be the preferred habitat of the King Cheetah. Meanwhile, Kruger Park held considerable promise. It was, after all, the size of Wales, a fact of logistics that powerfully influenced our decision to use a hot-air balloon. Calculated to fire media and public enthusiasm alike, it had the deliberate intention of bringing to the search a further two thousand pairs of eyes that virtually accounted for the entire Park, all 21,000 substantial square kilometres of it!

The aerial search was based on a simple principle. Any aerial map of Kruger National Park will demonstrate that it roughly resembles a patchwork quilt. A profusion of firebreaks, tracks and roads laces its expanse, roughly dividing it up into large hexagonal, triangular, rectangular or pear-shaped tracts of land. Non-steerable hot-air balloons allow a minimum of self-control, dependent as they are on every caprice of the wind. Therefore, in selecting one such area on our map, we'd take off in the balloon from a given point on the perimeter and simply let it drift with the wind, either at an angle, or straight across towards an opposing point. In relation to the direction of the wind, if it remained steady and was not too capricious, the objective could be estimated with reasonable accuracy. Accordingly, it was paramount that a flight should be planned beforehand from a map in conjunction with information about wind direction. This was measured first thing each morning and again, before every flight, with the help of a small helium-filled balloon.

Keeping as much as possible to the firebreaks and tracks, the retrieve crew had the unenviable task of tracking and following the balloon from the ground, assisted by the map with the "envisaged" flight pattern marked on it. For this purpose we always employed two of our four-wheel drives along opposite routes, thus ensuring that at least one retrieve crew got to the balloon as it landed—beforehand if possible. Needless to say this was of particular importance given the special problems associated with flying over a large game reserve filled with wildlife. Natural uncultivated bush and an abundance of wild inhabitants present very different conditions for the balloonist to green and pleasant farmland where the nearest candidate for what can be classified "wildlife" is someone's prize Charolais bull! Ideal flying condi-

198

Floating over Kruger Park — the first search for a specific type of animal using a hot-air balloon.

tions constituted little more than the slightest breeze during the coolest hours of daylight. But it wasn't always that straightforward. A brisk build-up of wind, or a dramatic change in direction could suddenly take the balloon on to a totally different course to the one it had been travelling. It disrupted the ground crew's navigation, not to mention the concentration of whoever it was in the balloon, Paul or myself, looking for a certain striped feline. Having radio communication with the ground didn't necessarily help. Whooshed off by some wilful gust behind a high ridge of kopjes, or down into a deep-graded gully, the special frequency we transmitted on would often fade out, causing complete loss of radio contact.

The hotter it became through the morning and into the afternoon, the more the thermals played havoc with the craft's equilibrium. One other thorny problem, the scale of which strangers to Africa can hardly appreciate, played havoc with more than just the balloon's equilibrium. Great matted patches of thornbush which in parts of Kruger Park lie across the ground like grey, menacing inland seas, could be lethal to delicate-skinned balloons. Naturally enough we avoided landing in them at all costs. As we were not permitted to carry firearms the possibility of an encounter with a large predator would have made an already prickly situation even pricklier. Believe me, ballooning elsewhere can't quite come up to ballooning in Africa! Certainly, for us, no other means of aerial transport could have suited our purposes better.

Our objective—with Paul and I taking turns on flights as spotter—was to cover from the air the South Central District between Oliphants in the north and Tshokwane, roughly ninety kilometres to the south, and right across the reserve as far west as the Timbavati River. There were always two people per flight, the pilot and the spotter. The lighter the load, the better the going. Thus, with only the pilot having to take care of the business of flying the bubble—with red and yellow stripes, it hung in the blue sky like a giant orange lollipop—and keeping open communications with the ground, the spotter was able to examine the country below without hindrance, camera around neck, ubiquitous binoculars in hand. And seeing was believing. Floating in a dreamlike hush at a height above ground usually between 50 and 100 metres, one could see for miles across the veldt in any direction; only the intermittent burst of the burner to keep our descent in check cutting the stillness. Sometimes in the clear, pristine air—so seemingly unpolluted and free of any matter we might have been suspended in a vacuum—bush and animals looked close enough to touch. Viewing was excellent and spotting continuously for a particular type of animal never seemed to be a chore.

Our "flight crew" from the Pioneer Balloon Club joined us two at a time at weekly intervals. The pilots included businesswoman Jeanette Van Ginkel, the "Beryl Markham" of the balloon ways, and a British civil engineer, Jim Burgess, who with his assistant Leslie, brought an individualism which was never at odds with the ability of each to work as equal members of a team. Our "co-pilots", Roger Newby and Bill Harrab, mostly operated with ground crew as navigators. Ginger-bearded Bill, who perpetually wore a bright red fishing hat to conceal the thinning growth on his scalp, to an unnerving degree had the ability to make one laugh with just a glance! With the daily risk we ran of flying into hostile territory, Bill's colleagues appeared not to consider him a "safe" bet when in control of a balloon because he was found of playing practical jokes when airborne. As he now manages the only Balloon Safari Company in southern Africa he obviously knew what he was doing.

We were indeed fortunate with our team, balloonists included, and especially fortunate with their humour and enthusiasm. Only two members could be suspected of being there for reasons different to everyone else's. One of them wanted to be the first to pilot a balloon over Kruger Park; the other wanted to exercise an inflated sense of authority by an obsessive use of the "walkie-talkie", the last thing one needs during an aerial search for an elusive animal! A fully inflated balloon when up and flying magnifies voices to such an extent that even the most quietly spoken words will carry loud and clear down to and along the ground, like an echo—the surest way to force animals into cover.

The local ranger appointed a Shangaan game scout by name of Salius to accompany the balloon sorties as a member of the ground crew. Over steaming cups of rooibos tea—the bush-tea made from a wild plant, since early times, by the indigenous population of southern Africa—many a tactical discussion was had with the ranger who himself participated in a few dawn launches and who helpfully stored the considerable bulk that constituted the balloon's gas supplies. Yes, we were certainly fortunate in the response we received and especially the response from the general public.

The King Cheetah had been sighted and photographed in Kruger Park on three separate occasions, each time by a tourist. With this in mind, a leaflet campaign, timed to work in with the search, mustered a veritable army of spotters the length and breadth of the Park. Aimed at the public, it brought just the response we had hoped for! Unique causes demand unique courses, after all, and an aerial search using anything other than a balloon would not have elicited the same response from ordinary people. For such a

Balloon search with Kruger Game Park Scout, Salius.

''needle-in-a-haystack'' search over such a wide area, our apparently eccentric choice of transport became a simple marketing ploy. Paul and I needed all the help we could get. We had everything to gain by urging tourists to watch for King

202

Help the King Cheetah expedition in its search

This graceful, majestic King Cheetah is now being sought in the park. This photograph was taken in the game reserve in 1975.

A search party is now using a hot-air balloon to find a King Cheetah — a uniquely formed and coloured animal — in the game reserve. The one in the game reserve (the same animal you see above) is presumably the only King Cheetah in the park and also in South Africa.

The King Cheetah resembles an ordinary cheetah physically, but its colour patern is quite different. Its unique qualities are:

1. Three broad stripes down its back.
2. Bold black irregular blotches on its side and legs.

If you see this animal please indicate the spot on the map with an X and write your name and camp. Hand this to the nearest game ranger.

Name . . . .

Camp . . . .

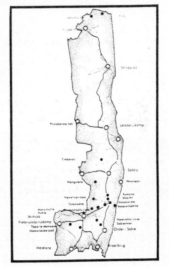

One of the thousands of printed handbills distributed throughout Kruger Park to all visitors during the expedition's balloon search — the first of its kind ever undertaken.

203

Cheetahs while out game-spotting, for the normal tarred tourist routes which they drove along every day were well away from our areas of operation.

Thousands of handbills, urging visitors to help the King Cheetah Expedition in its search, were printed by a major newspaper sponsor and distributed randomly throughout the Park. Bundles of handbills were also deposited at rest-camp offices and at all the Park's entrances for distribution to visitors entering the Park. In each handbill the objectives of the balloon search were outlined and the King Cheetah's physical attributes, especially its stripes and blotches, were described. A coloured illustration, based on one of the photographs taken of the animal in the Park, and a map of the reserve were included. In the event of a sighting the visitor was requested to fill in the relevant details—name, rest camp, and map reference—and to hand them to the nearest ranger or expedition member.

Two of our keenest canvassers were Jan and Willie. In between balloon flights and trading under the apt nicknames "Shutterbug" and "Gentle Giant", they were shrewdly instrumental in launching a daily "CB chat show" among the Park tourists. They reiterated the aims of the search and, most important, showed how each person could help the search team. The response was gratifying and gave us a very good idea of the strength of public interest in the King Cheetah. Considering how nearly every second car entering Kruger at the time had a CB radio, this was an ideal way, especially in conjunction with the leaflet campaign, to reach people quickly over a vast area. In no time at all Willie and Jan seemed to have had the entire Park radioed for action. They even picked up a fellow somewhere in the faraway backlands of my native Queensland! Heaven knows what he must have made of it all. He was probably having difficulty coming to terms with the existence of that Australian State's very own mysterious striped cat, the tiger-cat—assuming he'd heard of it—let alone King Cheetahs and balloons halfway across the globe!

The first time I went up in the balloon I found the experience exhilarating. The novelty may have worn off there hadn't have been some august objective to justify my being lifted skywards in a wicker basket again and again, but I think not; and certainly not in the location we had chosen, for it was tantamount to gliding through paradise. But ballooning has its mundane aspects as well. The only really involved aspect of it is the setting-up procedure, before take-off, when the balloon is inflated. With practice and the right weather conditions there's really little to it. Only a few of our attempts had to be delayed and that was because of sudden and strong gusts of wind. It wasn't possible to work on the principle that we had all day. In the tropics and sub-tropics ballooning is very much restricted to the cooler hours, which generally means from dawn till mid-morning, to around 9.30 at the outside, and again in the afternoon from about 3.30 until, say, 5.30 when the light begins to fade noticeably. Thus, about four to six hours flying time in any given day was all we could anticipate. One may as well discount the time between 10am and 3pm when temperatures soar to dizzy heights regardless of the season. This is the time animals mostly "lie up" to escape the heat—so too should balloons.

Before the balloon was ready to get under way a strict code of practice in setting up prior to take-off had to be observed. With the wind readings recorded and the general direction in which we wanted to fly decided, a suitably positioned clearing in a chosen area would be singled out where the balloon envelope could be stretched flat across the ground without us having to worry about fabric tearing on spindly bits of rock and scrub. With the balloon a lifeless skin at this stage, flapping the walls of the envelope up and down will loosen the fabric enough to get the air circulating throughout it before inflating it fully with air heated by the balloon's burner. With the basket lying on its side, the flame from the burner is directed straight at the mouth of the envelope which must be held open at the moment of inflation as widely and rigidly as possible to allow the heated air to flow without restriction into the balloon. As it inflates so the crew at the other end work furiously to hold down the crown of the balloon with the aid of a tow rope, trying to keep it steady and on the ground as it begins to swell and take shape. Then the balloon's rigging is clipped onto the basket. Those who have hold of the tow rope at the crown slacken off slowly and allow the large, pear-shaped monster to billow right out and rise gradually before eventually standing upright of its own accord. With the crew grabbing hold of the basket so as to prevent the craft from being wafted away in its swollen entirety, there is just sufficient time for pilot and passenger to clamber aboard before being wafted heavenwards. Before we were given charge of it the balloon was described to us as being something like five stories high and so it seemed to be, once upright and ready for take-off. When up and away, however, it floated like thistledown.

Generally speaking, the average distance covered by the balloon on any one flight was about 25 kilometres, occasionally as much as 45 kilometres. Usually the visibility was excellent, with large herds of game easily seen at almost any distance. By the same token, individual animals, from steenboks to hyenas and jackals, could be spotted with little difficulty. Jackals would turn madly skittish on being caught out in the open by the balloon, zig-zagging furiously away in even-paced spurts as if at each burst of the burner they were shocked anew. Hyenas, although scarcely altering their demeanour, never hung around for long either, loping off in that characteristic way of theirs without even stopping to look up. Lions, on the other hand, would glance up momentarily before slowly, almost reluctantly, turning and trotting away. Only the little steenbok reacted without a sense of urgency; but then, that is in its nature, the buck, as finely drawn as porcelain, too lovely and too innocent, according to the Bushmen, to know fear or suspicion. Birds just seemed to gaze back at us when we got near any of them, with a kind of resigned, half-stunned air born either of wonder or of a simple acceptance of man's eccentricity.

Below us, like an intricate web, stretched an abundance of game trails, a feature of wild Africa one can't fully appreciate until one has had the chance to view the open bush in quiet, unhurried seclusion from the air. In every sense of the phrase we enjoyed a bird's-eye view of the country with so many species of wildlife regularly promenading below us in a day from buffaloes and impalas in huge herds, wildebeest, more intimate groups of waterbuck or kudus, troops of zebras, massive elands in shy pairs, right down to an inscrutable-faced ratel, or honeybadger, the bravest of the brave, wobbling its self-important way across the veld. A regular sight was a sounder of warthog, one minute grubbing for roots, the next taking to flight with their tails ever perpendicular; another was the dainty klipspringer, sometimes two, perfectly balanced on an immense boulder or rocky outcrop; and even shy duikers, hardly ever more than one or two at a time, running for their lives like rabbits, diving in and out of the grass—as their Afrikaans name for "diver" suggests—with heads down, never stopping to look back. As a rule, those generally tolerant colossi of the plain, the elephants, never appeared to turn a hair of their tails when we floated by. On one occasion, however, an extremely irritated bull, which was courting a cow in a nearby herd, gave chase. Flapping huge ears often aptly described as resembling giant maps of Africa, his trunk raised defiantly, he charged along below us peering intently upwards and trumpeting sternly, now and then stopping to wave his trunk furiously above his head as though admonishing us for our indelicate intrusion.

I was surprised to see how, from a certain distance up, such distinctly marked animals as the giraffe and the zebra seemed to lose their distinctive colours and patterns, the zebra's lines being scarcely visible at all. A strange phenomenon? Not at all. Conspicuously patterned as zebras undoubtedly are, they may also be notoriously inconspicuous in the wild, as has been observed by many seasoned hunters and travellers through the years, with their distinct black and white—or more precisely blacky-brown and cream—markings readily merging, an optical effect that helps break up their shape and allows them to blend in with their surroundings. From the air this optical effect is merely accentuated. It is a phenomenon of physics that the impact of light on an object will often give a false result. Field observations of animals can seem relatively easy, until one has tried looking at animals in the wild at night and from the air. Certainly it highlighted the difficulty of seeing another equally distinctive striped animal, namely the King

Cheetah! So far we hadn't seen a spotted cheetah or a leopard even, and it was not for want of looking either.

The thorn bush cover mentioned earlier was something Paul and I weren't nearly as conscious of in Tuli as we were in Kruger. In parts of the reserve, from just a hundred feet or so above the ground, we photographed vast two- and three- acre patches of thorn thicket that from the balloon appeared below us as just a grey mass. With neither leaf nor strip of green to speak of, each branch was smothered from end to end by long, needle-like white thorns. Such country, I need hardly say, spells big trouble for hot-air balloons. The flight that afternoon had been a long one of about forty kilometres undertaken in ideal viewing conditions; all it had needed to make it perfect was a King Cheetah. A dramatic shift in course changed all that in a matter of moments. The craft had begun to drift menacingly towards this thick thorn country; there was "thorn as far as the eye could see" I was told later. Gas was low, and to go any further to try to overshoot it could spell disaster. It was decided to bring the craft down while the bush was still comparatively open.

According to Paul the pilot executed a beautifully manoeuvred landing, dropping neatly into a narrow clearing sandwiched between two inhospitable tracts of land scattered with thorn trees and gullies sufficient enough to indicate what had awaited them if they had flown on. But with the balloon acting rather like a square-rig in full sail, within moments of touching down it was caught suddenly by a powerful gust of wind. A violent twist sideways dragged the craft towards an isolated stand of thorn. Having already extricated themselves from the basket when it lurched over, the strength of the two men had not been enough to hold it.

In the meantime, with radio communications between ground crew and balloon having packed up in the last few minutes of flight, neither of the retrieve vehicles was able to locate the balloon by sight because of the rolling nature of the country. The area it had vanished into was covered with a densely-packed bush of undulating scrub and tall trees draped like a shaggy-pile carpet across a progression of narrow ridges and ditches that killed

After crash-landing the balloon, the crew tries to disentangle its remains.

visibility as much as it did radio link-up. In a vehicle it was, for the most part, virtually impassable. The balloon, we discovered later, was not very far away from us.

The back-up retrieve crew was some distance away from me in "Ingwe", on the other side of a creek-bed, the last place I had seen the balloon from my Landcruiser. I hoped Paul or the pilot had spotted "Ingwe". Unlike Landrovers, which are faithful to their classic sand colour and are "at one" with the bush, the white Landcruiser, from the air, stood out rather like a neon sign in that environment. Now as I urged it on through the failing afternoon light and the uncompromising bush, frantically hoping I was heading in the right direction, the unmistakeable odour of lion began to grow menacingly stronger in my nostrils. With Paul unarmed, in accordance with Kruger Park policy, my mission acquired a new urgency.

Paul, too, had scented lion nearby, so I discovered later. It was believed by us balloonists that in such a situation, igniting the burner at 30-second intervals would not only act as a helpful beacon for the ground crew, it would also deter certain bush-whacking animals from fulfilling any untoward designs on the balloon's cargo. With an increasingly fidgety pilot, a badly ensnared balloon envelope, little or no gas, and still no sign of the ground crew even though the balloon had been down a good twenty minutes or more, Paul wasn't about to hang around to find out. When an imperative grunt suddenly punctuated the stillness at a distance far too close for comfort, Paul bundled a by-now near-gibbering pilot up to the top of a twenty-foot windmill, fortuitously situated close-by, and then immediately struck out on his own for a dirt track he'd seen from the top of it. Reaching a cutting that at first glance appeared to meander nowhere in particular, he crossed to a creek-bed where from atop a bank he could just make out the rear of a Landrover. The sun was shining on it and its colour caught his eye. It was ''Ingwe''.

It took us about half an hour to free the balloon. Although reparable, damage to the envelope was extensive for it had moulded itself around a thorn tree like a sheet of melted plastic. Looking rather like a pincushion, the rips that had developed were fortunately tiny ones. None fell below what is known as the balloon's ''horizon'' and this indicated that there was no structural damage. Back at camp, in the fading light, a bevy of balloonists—experts at this sort of thing we were assured—glued and snipped and sewed well into the night. Another dawn launch was but eight hours away.

Blowing in the Wind

"A needle in a haystack!", was how an interviewer on BBC TV's "Nationwide" programme once put it, in a general reference to our looking for an exclusive and elusive cat in the southern African bush. Whimsically recalling this expression when I was in the balloon one bright morning, a hundred feet up in the air over Kruger Park, it seemed only too appropriate as I peered down hopefully into the bushveld which, after weeks of aerial search, seemed to be wearing its secrecy increasingly like a shroud. Not one cheetah, not one leopard had we seen, though both animals were common sights on ground recces, given the elusiveness of each cat in the wild. Thus we could only conclude that they were keeping well to cover in amongst scrub, thornbush and the like. Even lions were sometimes difficult to spot from the balloon, despite their size and nonchalance when compared to other mammals, resembling as they often do at night, sandy-coated donkeys. This dearth of big cats in general is nothing new in aerial search; we had just hoped it would be different using a balloon. After all, no other aircraft is less in conflict with nature. Game were far less inclined to bolt from it as they would a fixed-wing plane or helicopter; even a "microlite", with its capacity to operate in extremes of temperature would, I daresay, have annoyed game animals because of its high-pitched, lawnmower whine. It was a question of time and chance—and luck. It was, therefore, a wry commentary on the balloon search that, concurrent with it, there should be news reaching us of observers on the ground claiming to have seen the King Cheetah!

Some reports of King Cheetahs certainly didn't strike us as idle fancies. One tourist told us: "I'm a city man, a doctor, and I saw what looked to me like a leopard walking with a cheetah". It was an enchanting observation. Bearing in mind that people were viewing from a distance and unprepared for such a sight, there

211

could have been no more apt description of the sight of a King Cheetah walking with a spotted cheetah. Such an observation offers ample room, indeed, to reflect as much on the old argument for the King Cheetah being a hybrid leopard/cheetah as on the folklore legend, peculiar to Manicaland in Eastern Zimbabwe, of the lithe "leopard-hyena" with dog-like spoor and slouching gait that was as feared as the *nsuifisi*. The King Cheetah sighting in question referred to an incident near Bangu, a windmill and game pool on the northern fringe of our area of search en route to the Gorge just south of the Oliphants, or Elephants river, thick bush country, flanking the Mozambique border. The sighting was made all the more credible by another sighting at the same place and at about the same time by two middle-aged businesswomen holiday-ing together in the reserve. About a week before the doctor's sighting they claimed to have watched from their car, while parked at the roadside at Bangu, a pair of big cats feeding off a dead impala. One they described as an ordinary spotted cheetah; the other and larger one had, in their own words," stripes running all along its spine". The three people concerned in these two sightings knew nothing of any other professed sighting of an unusual big cat near or at the same spot.

One should bear in mind that the persuasive element of publicity could play its part so well that, with the balloon exercise so promi-nent and Park visitors being actively urged to keep their eyes open for King Cheetahs, anyone could sub-consciously conjure up in the mind's eye a King Cheetah where there was none—wish-fulfilment—pure and simple. We can all imagine the situation, even those of us who've never experienced anything like it. Having said that, it's always easier to play the sceptic than to give people the benefit of the doubt. One's own instinct is generally a reliable buttress anyway in gauging the validity or sincerity of such. Indeed, sometimes people had second thoughts about what they had reported, thus acting as their own censors.

This was not the case with the student son of one of the Park's maintenance officers, on holiday from college. After an afternoon's fishing in the Olifants River at Balule pump station, just a little

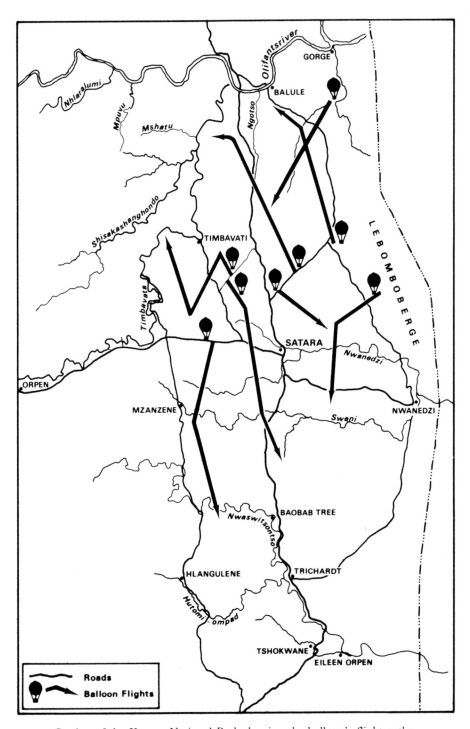

Section of the Kruger National Park showing the balloon's flight paths.

213

west of Bangu, he was driving home down the dirt road that follows the power line straight to Satara. About four to five kilometres along it, as he told his father later, he saw what looked to him exactly like a "heavy cheetah with stripes" cross over in front of him. As he drew closer, it lingered awhile before smartly vanishing back into the bush as abruptly as it had appeared. Bangu windmill is less than 10 kilometres from his sighting in what is, after all, a huge game park, and although there was a time lapse of some six months between the boy's sighting and the more recent ones at Bangu, his was worth serious consideration.

Another "sighting" with an authentic ring to it, occurred just about a month before Paul and I took our first trip to Kruger prior to the balloon search. This one concerned a woman who had leased a cottage in the Park; she was a great-niece of Sir Percy Fitz Patrick of *Jock Of The Bushveld* fame. Over dinner she told us how she and her teenage son were out driving along the Timbavati road at the back of Satara when they stopped at a popular waterhole. Almost immediately their eyes focused on a kill—impala it seemed like to them—at which two big cats were feeding. They seemed to be cheetahs, except that one was noticeably darker than the other and appeared to have thick, horizontal stripes along its back. Attracted by this strange looking animal, she attempted to manoeuvre the car closer but in the process disturbed the darker, striped one which straightaway slunk off into some thickish scrub at the side—in a manner, it struck both she and her son, particularly leopard-like—from where it proceeded to watch furtively while calling away its mate with the characteristic bird-like "chirrup" of the cheetah.

Sadly, no photographs were taken by anybody, despite the recent plethora of news about the King Cheetah and the expedition given out by the media and again later in Kruger about the balloon search. Neither were there any photographs to support the other sightings at Bangu and earlier at Balule, illustrating something about missed opportunities, quite apart from those where the witness is just totally unaware at the time that he or she has seen something rare and unusual. One couldn't help but wonder how

214

many other members of the public had had similar experiences down the years we'd never know about.

All the main rest camps in Kruger Park are equipped with an open-air theatre built with the simplicity of the classic Greek style. Thus, it was natural to go touring with the film of the King Cheetah. For people in general—who usually emptied the camp to come to our evening shows—seeing the King Cheetah alive before their eyes was devastating. They were spellbound by the realisation that here was that unknown quantity of the animal world many "experts" hadn't believed existed, a creature more magnificent than any cat they'd seen and one that justified its title. Never again could the King Cheetah be considered just a dusty old myth. Their enthusiasm was like a pep pill after a trying and unsuccessful series of balloon sorties. Never let it be said that seeing a King Cheetah alive on the screen is vastly different to looking for one in the wild! Indeed, there was a great deal of talk around this time of a film being made of the balloon exercise, through the good offices of the South African Nature Foundation under the patronage of the World Wildlife Fund. Negotiations went on for weeks, with messages flying back and forth between Cape Town and Skukuza. For one breathless moment our intermediary in the Foundation even had a camera crew on board a light plane bound for the Park... but it seems they got no further than Johannesburg. That there could be something special about a film of a unique balloon search for a unique cat in one of the world's premier game parks, against a backdrop of wildlife and bush scenery, was well recognised. Suffice it to say that prominent conservation bodies are no better placed than the rest of us when it comes to raising financial support!

Despite such minor setbacks, not to mention the lack of success so far as our main objective was concerned, camaraderie among the team remained high as the weeks progressed; and if ever there was a good reason to have fond memories of the balloon search in Kruger Park, this was certainly it. We found early evenings around the campfire, over a sundowner or two, the best time to unwind completely and chat about the day's events before the

Aerial shot from balloon, Kruger Park.

evening meal. The mood then was always warm and chummy and frequently high-spirited. Later on, when we could have as many as twelve or thirteen for dinner, things invariably took on the atmosphere of a party. It was because of this that I finished up learning how to turn mealie pap into a cordon bleu special under the expert tutelage of Jan Hamman, our prize-winning press photographer, who was an expert at cooking up this traditional staple food of ground maize meal so that it didn't resemble a tasteless blob. In fact, this was one of the more delightful human aspects of the whole exercise in Kruger: people pitching in whether ballooning or preparing the main meal of the day. Inevitably, a little evening "revelry" was seen as a bonus after a long day of endless action that had begun with the first balloon launch at dawn. For all that, the King Cheetah still remained the main topic

216

of conversation as not an evening went by without someone dropping in at the camp to hear about the latest events.

The bush is an endless source of fascination and contradiction. Yet game parks, though offering the same diversity of mood on the surface, may deceive us. A Kruger Park visitor, on seeing an otherwise healthy leopard with a torn and slightly bloodied ear, once told Paul, who happened to be in the same place at the same time, that something should be done immediately about "the poor, sweet animal's wound"! The fact that the poor sweet animal looked perfectly fit and able to continue ripping out throats for some time to come seemed to have passed her by. Probably she had first been convinced by Disney productions, then by successive trips through reserves and game parks in the cossetted confines of a limousine, that wild animals are not what the scientists make them out to be, and that a leopard is just another pussy-cat. Anthropomorphism in the extreme is as much a threat to the survival of wild animals as poaching, over-culling and unrestricted hunting, or destruction of habitats.

As September slipped away so did weather conditions deteriorate and before long we'd disbanded ballooning altogether. Not only were the winds with us in force, but temperatures in the lowveld had been increasing daily with the rapid approach of summer. To try to carry on ballooning in such conditions would have been futile. More than that however, the exercise had failed dismally in its main objective, to locate King Cheetah.

Conducting an aerial search from a balloon has its advantages: the ability to float slowly over the bush at a very short distance above the ground is one of them. But a hot-air balloon cannot be steered. Whatever method is chosen in a search of this kind, however, sophisticated modes of transport can't guarantee success any more than balloons—or even horses. Using helicopters, light planes or motorised gliders one may well end up scouring the wild for a year to no avail, yet in another time and place, after only a week perhaps, you may turn a corner and there is your quarry. You need luck in this game.

In their efforts to assist the expedition the Park authorities, as well

217

as the staff stationed in the reserve, had done us proud. Now, when I look back on that time, I need only recall the bizarre, drum-like call of those swaggering, comic birds that abound in Kruger Park, the big, red-beaked ground hornbills, and I'm back there plodding its ample expanse with them.

Ex Africa Semper

However it may be measured in degrees of success or failure, the balloon exercise was a triumph in media hype and co-operation. Looked at coldly, it was simply another milestone in an extraordinary expedition that had assured the King Cheetah a place in the public consciousness, had increased the current field knowledge of the animal, and had re-opened the question of its status. Now, with the winding up of the balloon search to conclude the most comprehensive fieldwork on the King Cheetah ever undertaken, the emphasis shifted.

A programme of selective breeding using common cheetahs from those areas of southern Africa demonstrated by our research to be King Cheetah habitats, offered every possibility of producing King Cheetahs under captive conditions. One of the tragic realities of modern Africa is the way its virgin habitats are being eroded. Much of her wildlife is now confined within artifical boundaries. But, even though reserves and game parks can only be samples of the old ecosystem where nature was free to operate unhindered by man-made strictures, they have become cornerstones of present-day wildlife conservation. Despite our urgings, however, nowhere was there in operation a specialised programme for selective breeding of the King Cheetah. Accidents, nonetheless, will happen.

Someone once wrote that Africa is the natural home of coincidence. On the 12th and 14th May 1981, little more than a year after the completion of our fieldwork, the first King Cheetahs to be bred in captivity, one male and one female, were born. Each was conceived of spotted cheetahs at the De Wildt Cheetah Breeding Station and Research Centre in South Africa, and was sired by the same male wild-caught as a cub in the Messina district of the northern Transvaal—the very area our research had pinpointed as part of the habitat range of the King Cheetah! The two

The King Cheetah pattern is standard across all specimens available for examination. The outstanding difference in markings between spotted cheetahs and King Cheetahs is strikingly demonstrated in this study of adolescent animals at the De Wildt Cheetah Breeding Station, South Africa.

mothers were sisters bred from parents, also wild-caught, which had come from the northern Transvaal and Namibia. They were not born within any planned programme; they were born, as it were, "by accident". The De Wildt Station had been vehemently opposed to investing time or money in what it considered a side issue to its main campaign: the study and breeding of cheetahs in general, to which all their resources were fully committed. Thus the births couldn't have come at a more fortuitous moment than if they had been planned by providence.

In the case of such a zoological oddity as the King Cheetah, fame can be a kind of safety net. The publicity that had surrounded our research and fieldwork had generated for the King Cheetah a notoriety that had permanently stripped it of its previous anonymity; it had almost become famous. It is ironic, therefore, that the pregnant mother of the female King Cheetah cub-to-be was sold off before she gave birth. Apparently her considerable climbing abilities, which had earned for her the nickname "Jumper", had posed a threat to the efficiency of breeding procedures at the Station. The cub, subsequently christened "Queenie", was born in a small, commercially orientated game park in Natal. Within a few weeks there was a five-figure price tag on her head. Some time later, it seems, "Queenie" was "transferred" back to the De Wildt Cheetah Breeding Station, a celebrity in her own right.

The births within two days of each other were to be the first of several. At the time of writing, eleven more King Cheetahs have since been born at the De Wildt Station from offspring of the same cheetah line; the latest was born in 1987. Only half of the original stock of thirteen cubs survive, demonstrating something of the high mortality rate of cheetahs in captivity as much as the strength of the genes producing the King Cheetah. And there have been other problems, some with hindsight predictable, others not.

De Wildt nestles on a shadowy South African outcrop overlooking the controversial homeland of Bophuthatswana. In response to the severe reductions in the cheetah population across Africa this century, it was established as part of a comprehensive programme for the propagation of captive cheetah. Starting with an original stock of cheetahs wild-caught in the northern Transvaal and Namibia, and with the help of an occasional enlightened farmer keen on capturing rather than shooting cheetahs, the skill of its breeding programme has enjoyed phenomenal success. Already adult offspring have been translocated to the semi-wild state. Thus, given the low levels of fertility and genetic variation that research studies have recorded in cheetahs, the unique success story of De Wildt would seem to be both good news for the cheetah and for captive breeding in general. But, admirable as that success may be, the captive breeding of cheetahs brings with it unique problems which, for many people, questions the very point of it.

Captive-bred cheetahs, more than any other cats, are particularly difficult to translocate successfully to the wild state simply because the specialised hunting skills best taught to cheetah cubs by their mother in natural, wild conditions, are virtually impossible to simulate successfully in captivity. This was why cheetahs used as hunting companions in the past were captured as adults for large royal stables when their hunting skills had been fully learned and tried, a custom that, unfortunately, resulted in the inevitable decline in numbers of cheetah breeding stock in the wild. After all, the specialised methods that the cheetah employs to chase, strangle and dissect its prey is unique to it; and its physique and internal organs are specially adapted to perform the kind of hunting skills that give this high-speed runner a better success rate of kills in the open savanna than any of its major competitors. Sadly, while cheetahs are being bred so successfully in captive breeding sanctuaries such as De Wildt, the fact remains that the few still left today in the wild in South Africa continue to be shot as persistently as ever, a tragic contradiction.

As guests of keeper Ann van Dyk who, while managing the centre for Pretoria Zoo, has been to a large degree responsible with vet David Meltzer for De Wildt's success, we spent an amiable and informative few days observing and, in a minor way, participating in the various methods employed in its breeding and research programme. The centre has good natural drainage with a fair cover

In this study of a King Cheetah, one can see how the cat's heavy markings would clearly be disadvantageous in open savanna, yet ideal camouflage in woodland and thornbush habitat.

of trees and bushy scrub, and is largely made up of spacious enclosures which fit in with the surrounding environment with respect to size, lay-out, and natural ambience. Its philosophy has been to keep the animals as wild as possible and to restrict human activity. In the breeding season at De Wildt males and females are isolated, except for mating purposes, with groups of males being released daily near the female enclosures to gauge and observe the onset of sexual receptivity. Hereafter, oestrous females are allowed to mate as much as desired for two to three days with a specified male. As for the maternity pens, strategically placed slits or "windows" in the boma-like high, brush fencing permit the observer to see inside without being seen; the aim is to avoid undue stress being placed on a nursing cheetah. The animals undergo regular veterinary checks, including blood counts and the like. Records are kept of each individual. In the case of a wild-caught cheetah, this includes a reference to its origin. This appeared to be

223

mostly in the northern Transvaal, a fact which was to prove pertinent with respect to the King Cheetah.

One particular study just being embarked upon at the time of our visit involved looking at the reproductive traits of male cheetahs in established populations. Cheetahs display a strikingly low level of fertility, particularly in captivity, due mostly, it had previously been thought, to stress induced by captive conditions. The study involved examination of semen collected by the electro-ejaculation method. With the animals having been first anaesthetized, then weighed, the ejaculation of individual males was stimulated with a small electro-charged rectal probe shaped like a phallus and inserted into the cheetah's rectum. This stimulated seminal flow and the ejaculate was then collected in a warmed vial. When the study was complete, some three years later, it was to confirm that the ejaculate quality in the male cheetah is poor; the cause, it has been held, is of either genetic consequence, a unique species norm, or possibly both. Sperm counts were shown to be as much as ten times lower than in other related species like the domestic cat, with a staggering 70 percent of the sperm deformed in physical character. Such findings in a mammal species are generally linked to pronounced infertility. For the first time they offered a logical explanation for the difficulties that have been encountered in the breeding of cheetahs since time immemorial. Together with the strikingly low levels of genetic variation that have been demonstrated to exist in southern African and east African cheetahs, it poses some intriguing questions. Where, for instance, does the King Cheetah fit in all this?

The modern species of cheetah is the most specialised of the big cats. The only species in its genus, *Acinonyx*, it has also shown remarkable uniformity in both type and markings throughout its formerly wide distribution over much of India, across Africa from the Cape to Cairo and all suitable regions between in south-west Asia. Smaller or paler spotting as is well known, or subtle variegations in coat base colour, do occur in response to the demands of environment. But notable pattern variations are uncommon enough in the cheetah to be considered rare. Indeed, the

224

appearance of spontaneous mutations in cheetahs during the five thousand years man has associated with them—in what is probably the most unique relationship ever known between man and beast—have been so rare, they are virtually non-existent. As the cheetah's Hindi name "spotted one" suggests, nothing remotely like the King Cheetah has ever been recorded. There exist no intermediate coat patterns to speak of between it and the spotted cheetah. No feline species in Africa or Asia, in fact, has been known to produce, at intervals, a consistently uniform and singularly distinctive pattern variant displaying such a marked divergence from the norm, a variant which is also consistent in its occurrence over a wide but well defined geographic area. The uniformity of the King Cheetah's coat pattern, similar in thirty-eight specimens recorded so far south of the Zambezi in a portion of southern Africa where the common spotted cheetah has been nearly exterminated, is unparalleled among big cats. This makes more significant the recent research which indicates that all cheetahs are virtually genetic twins, for they have levels of genetic variation which are among the lowest in any known mammal species.

Genetic uniformity in any species hampers its ability to adapt to severe ecological upheavals and changes by reducing the natural buoyancy of variation within the species. The animal will not cope well with new viruses. Competing successfully for survival becomes more difficult. Such is the cheetah's genetic uniformity that even skin grafts transplanted from one cheetah to another in one study, were readily accepted without subsequent rejection. With its reproductive abilities no less affected, with low sperm counts and deformed sperm as demonstrated in the De Wildt study, it is hardly surprising that the conception rate of the cheetah, both in the wild and in captivity, should be low. On the other hand cub mortality is high; in the wild it is as much as 70 percent and in captivity it is higher than in most other large mammals. The breeding of cheetahs has always been very difficult. Akbar the Great, the sixteenth-century Moghul emperor and father of Jahangir, is renowned in history for having kept cheetahs and hunting with them. It may not be well known that he went to great lengths to encourage breeding among his cheetahs. Eventually he achieved success: one litter—and it was the only documented cheetah litter to be born in captivity until 1956!

It is noteworthy that such significant findings should occur in the one big cat considered to be the least adaptable in times of ecological stress and the least able to produce spontaneous aberrations and mutations. The cheetah has been a hunting companion for man from as early as B.C. 3000, in Sumeria, to recent times— and yet it is the one big cat science has taken the longest to know. Is it not remarkable, therefore, that no written or pictorial record has come down to us of an unusual cat remotely resembling the King Cheetah? The high esteem accorded to these cats by their royal masters in times past has been generously chronicled and colourfully depicted on everything from ancient Egyptian wall-paintings such as on the tomb of Ramses II to rich Renaissance tapestries. Akbar even raised one to the rank of ''chief'' following an exceptional kill it had made, further ordering that a drum be beaten in front of it in its honour whenever it went out. It is surely logical to assume that a cheetah as singularly different and handsome as the King Cheetah would have excited enough royal attention for it to have been recorded for posterity. After all, such literary observations on the rare and unusual in the wild animal kingdom are well known as those of Jahangir ably demonstrate.

Despite this some scientists are still disposed to regard the King Cheetah as little more than a colour variation which occasionally occurs among ordinary cheetahs, supported by the birth of King Cheetahs in captivity from normal spotted cheetahs—a simple pattern aberration in other words, comparable to numerous other aberrations commonly found in leopards in Africa. It must be remarked, however, that on this very question of the incidence of aberrations in the leopard and the cheetah, the two species couldn't be more different. The infinite degree of variability in ground colour and markings present in the leopard, for instance, has led modern taxonomists to describe and name as many as thirty sub-species, as well as innumerable aberrations. It is much the same

226

Lena and Paul Bottriell at Loskop Cheetah Sanctuary. Examining spotted cheetahs for the appearance of any blotches or stripes that could be considered an intermediate stage between the common cheetah and King Cheetah was an essential part of research.

with the serval, which displays such diversity in its pattern of barring, spotting and base colouring that the servaline—the small-spotted or speckled serval in which the spots are so minute it appears to be almost plain coated—was for a long time considered to be a separate species (it actually represents the extreme end of a very wide colour and pattern range, there being intermediates of all stages between the two basic types). The contrast between these and the cheetah and the King Cheetah couldn't be greater.

It has been suggested that the King Cheetah represents a similar genetic phenomenon to that which produces the change in the domestic cat from the "wild type" striped or mackerel tabby to the classic blotched tabby. Parallels have also been drawn with white tigers and even white lions. But white lions, for instance, have intermediate stages. Some lions even have white socks! Achilles of the Timbavati pride is a prime example of this. Tigers have white bellies, but sometimes the white extends to most parts of the legs and half-way up the chest; this is arguably an intermediate stage. Furthermore, both white lions and white tigers are only single, flat-colour deviations appearing in locations relatively small in extent when compared to the King Cheetah's habitat-range. As for the tabby, four distinct forms are recognised as occurring naturally. The tabby also has a universal distribution. The King Cheetah has only ever appeared in a specific geographic area of Africa south of the Zambezi in southern Africa. Moreover, the King Cheetah's pattern has basically five distinct points of difference from the ordinary cheetah: embossed stripes and blotches strikingly raised above the base hair; longer, silkier hair; striped and ringed tail; bold black on cream or ivory colouring, and a longer mane that remain virtually unchanged across thirty-eight specimens. These differences are hardly comparable to a single colour, or more precisely to the single pattern change from just "wild-type" stripes to blotches, such as occurs in the tabby.

These comparisons invite several questions. How can such a marked variation in the King Cheetah come from a single recessive gene, as has been suggested since the first specimens were born in captivity—significantly out of cheetahs from the King Cheetah's suggested geographic area? Just what significance does its continued occurrence have? How is it that with such marked physical differences from the common spotted cheetah it can so regularly appear with such a uniformity of pattern? Why indeed are there no intermediate coat patterns between it and the ordinary cheetah? King Cheetahs are without question the most unexpected, uniquely patterned big cats to be chronicled in modern times. Their appearance is unprecedented. No variation in any felid species can compare with theirs. The markings alone are strikingly dissimilar to anything recorded before or since the first documented skin was collected—dark markings, best suited to thornbush and woodland, approaching a forest environment which is not generally associated with the cheetah. No ordinary cheetah this, no simple deviation from the norm in a single colour change. Genotype aside, the King Cheetah is essentially different and not just in the way a black jaguar differs from the average spotted jaguar, or a ginger leopard from the average leopard. With these we are simply looking at a basic colour deviation: black in the one instance, with the jaguar's spots still evident; a gingery overlay, a wash of ginger over the cat's markings in the other.

The King Cheetah, on the other hand, is not just different in colouring, striking as that may be. Its fur is longer; it has a slightly bigger mane as a result; it is a "big" cheetah. These are characteristics worthy of note on their own. More important, however, is the regular appearance, only south of the Zambezi in a wide but well defined geographic area in southern Africa, of the standard King Cheetah pattern, a pattern which makes it unique among big cats: a uniform combination of bold black-brown markings, embossed, or raised above, a cream base on a coat characterised by softer, silkier, longer hair; broad, distinctive stripes running down the spine; heavy irregular blotches on flanks and hindquarters; and a striped and ringed tail. This combination of features is consistent in all King Cheetah specimens available for examination (assuming an acceptable degree of deviation between members of the same patterned species or race, such as we see in Grevy's zebra and the Siberian tiger, among others).

The results of the hair analysis add a significant parameter which is difficult to judge accurately. Should that, too, be put down to coincidence, a smudge on the slide perhaps, or a fluke? Does it correlate with supposed evolutionary traits in the cheetah? What of the De Wildt King Cheetah cub's mother, "Jumper", with her leopard-like climbing abilities, so remarkable in an animal celebrated as a sprinter but not as a climber? Is there more to the "hyena-leopard" description of the King Cheetah in the *nsuifisi* legend from Zimbabwe? With its dark markings and heavier build making woodland and forest ideal camouflage for it, how much effect could the increased ultra-violet in those conditions be having on the development of the King Cheetah's patterning? What, too, may be the added effect on that development of the minerals in the soil, consumed via the vegetation by its prey? Too many oddities in nature have been put down to coincidence, leaving the way open for yet another missed opportunity.

The mounted King Cheetah specimen in the Natal Museum, Pietermaritzburg, South Africa labelled 'Coopers Cheetah': one of the first five King Cheetahs collected in Southern Rhodesia. Mounted in 1929 by Rowland Ward, this world famous firm of game measures listed and illustrated the King Cheetah as a separate species as recently as 1980.

Never was there a more lucid illustration in the King Cheetah of evolution happening, or perhaps struggling to happen, before our eyes! Mutations, after all, provide the genetic variations upon which natural selection can act. Is it impossible to watch a species at different stages of its development? Does not a sub-species in the making first logically manifest itself as a mutation? In such a process, environment and geography play significant parts—witness the increased proportion of dark-coloured moths in areas of high pollution in Britain due to predation by birds on the more obvious, lighter moths. The leopard's "rosettes" aptly mimic the light-dappled, shady cover in a chosen tree. The dainty shoulder barring of the serval neatly echoes the spindly, spiked tops of the thatch or tambookie grass with which it regularly associates in the grasslands and watered habitats of Africa it frequents. Camouflage is a com-

230

mon condition of survival. In a wooded, forested environment so suited to its heavy dark markings, the King Cheetah's stripes and blotches seen from a tree above them would perfectly mimic the network of branches and foliage in shadow around them. Thick barred stripes and large jig-sawed blotches constitute an ideal dual-camouflage, useful in attack and, equally, useful as a defence mechanism against efficient tree-dwelling hunters like the leopard. Such markings are perfectly suited to the heavier wooded cover of the forested environment.

It is argued that King Cheetahs cannot be awarded sub-species status as they do not occupy a separate geographic area. But, as far as the naming and describing of species and races is concerned, the definition of a separate geographic area is as yet not precise. The species of rhino particular to the island of Java is as separated, specifically, from the smaller Sumatran species, as the two islands are by the Sunda Strait. Few natural barriers in Africa can so precisely and so completely delineate and isolate one geographic area from the other. No better is this demonstrated than with the geographic areas ascribed to the seven species and sub-species of zebra. These have all been named and described from a portion of the African continent; and if the mountain zebra of the Cape had not been exterminated throughout most of its former range their ranges would all still widely overlap.

The suggested geographic range for the King Cheetah inter-connects between areas of thorn forest and woodland of mostly high elevation in a triangle of country sweeping south through eastern Zimbabwe to Botswana, thence along the Limpopo River to the Lebombo Mountains flanking Kruger Park. These areas are connected as much by direct geographic link as they are by vegetation type, topography, climate, and even soil. The mighty Zambezi River, which once divided the two former Rhodesias, is a formidable northern boundary that since time immemorial has been an impassable barrier for wildlife, preventing migration of cheetahs north or south of it. The Limpopo River in the south provides another natural barrier for most of its course, thus accounting for the fewer reports of King Cheetahs in the wild in South

Balloon search camp-site, Satara, Kruger Park.

Africa. Westward beyond the woodland country of Tuli in north-east Botswana spreads the vast Kalahari where the King Cheetah's markings would naturally be disadvantageous. Lastly, adjacent to the lonely, isolated strip of forest and thornbush running the length of western Mozambique, is the lush chain of hills and mountains in Zimbabwe's secluded border region. As this is the provenance of the most notable number of wild King Cheetah sightings and skins recorded to date it may well represent the nerve centre of the King Cheetah's geographic area, as much as its eastern boundary. Intensive settlement and development and the consequent slaughter of cheetahs elsewhere has created its own barrier.

Never is nature more adaptable than when under threat. Just as today's ecosystem is in retreat, so too is the cheetah retreating. Its old habitat has been severely eroded by urban and agricultural development. Driven away increasingly from the savannas the cheetah must adapt. That it can is evident in Kora in central Kenya where spotted cheetahs have adapted to a thornbush habitat. In the King Cheetah we could be witnessing a development more profound, as Miklos Kretzoi judged so presciently more than half a century ago. It appears to be one of those rare opportunities to watch nature in the process of evolving a distinct and absolute pattern change in response to pressing environmental needs; mere colour phases may be succeeded by the possible development of a new race of cheetah which, one day, may attain species status. Having to adapt their way of hunting to a wooded/forested environment, where speed would not be as advantageous as it would in more open habitats, may be detrimental for the species as a whole but favourable for the striped individuals which would be better camouflaged. What may have interfered with the process, to an extent we will never be able to judge accurately, is the wholesale slaughter of cheetahs over the past eighty years in the areas of southern Africa where King Cheetahs have appeared.

Cheetahs continue to be shot in the wild in southern Africa as, ironically, they are being increasingly bred in captivity. Thus, with the difficulties that belabour attempts to introduce captive-bred cheetahs into the wild, cheetah sanctuaries, at worst, are seen by their critics to be breeding little more than ''zoo animals; at best, they are recognised as an enormous pool of material for research. It is in this latter respect that the King Cheetah, if it is to serve no other purpose, can play a vibrant part. Given the cheetah's low level of genetic variation, a breeding programme involving King Cheetahs might be one means of increasing genetic variation— heterozygosity as it is called by the scientists—in todays cheetah populations. In this way, perhaps, the cheetah's vulnerability and mortality in infancy may be reduced, giving it a better chance to cope in a time of ecological upheaval. In a litter of cheetahs, recently born at Britain's Whipsnade Zoo of East African and southern African parents, a reduction in the mortality rate was noted. Levels of genetic variation in the East African cheetah are known to be fractionally higher than levels in a captive South African cheetah. For the immediate present, however, the choice lies with those actively involved in the breeding programme at the cheetah station in South Africa which houses the only King

233

Cheetahs known to have been born in captivity. In Kruger Park, following our research work there, two further King Cheetahs— adolescents presumed to be siblings—were sighted and photographed in the very area of the reserve near Tshokwane from where we operated on our previous searches. Unfortunately, captive-bred cats are currently the only King Cheetahs the casual observer can be guaranteed to see. Kruger Park, it will be remembered, is the size of Wales.

Evolution is a controversial process. Evolutionary theory itself is based strictly on circumstantial evidence. How long, for example, does an aberration remain an aberration? For how long and how often must the same unique and distinctive standard pattern turn up so that more than one appears in a litter? No "mere" mutation, after all, would become a legend in native folklore—unless it represented something more significant, more lasting, than just a temporary hiccup in the evolutionary process. The legendary King Cheetah is alive today. The myth has been speedily de-mythified. For reasons nature has exercised since time immemorial, the world may be witnessing in it the gradual emergence, the evolution, of a new race of cheetah. We may have caught evolution in action. Just what route the King Cheetah's future takes from here lies as much in fickle man's hands as resilient nature's.

At a certain time during the festive days approaching New Year 1987 a freak hail-storm struck the De Wildt Cheetah Breeding Station. Fierce lightning either preceded or followed it. Several cheetahs were reported killed. It is said by the Africans that many of man's actions are contrary to the will of the gods. An example often quoted is the harnessing of the mighty Zambezi River by the great Kariba Dam. The original "coffer-dams" as they were known had just been completed when tremendous floods suddenly swept over the area, wiping out the construction to date and thereby vindicating the local tribesmen's assertions that the River Gods would visit their wrath on those who tampered with their kingdom. They say it is the same with nature and the animals prized above all else for their uniqueness or special beauty— animals such as the King Cheetah. The gods, it seems, do not easily give up what they consider their own! And so they sent lightning and hail to show their displeasure at the caging up, like commonplace chickens, of the great cats born to run.

It may indeed be so; just as Africa may indeed be the natural home of coincidence. But one thing, among others, is certain: the cheetah is struggling for its very existence. It is for this reason and no other that we may well be witnessing the evolution of a new geographic race of cheetah. Ultimately, if time and the gods allow, a new felid species will walk the earth. It will be called, as it should be called, the King Cheetah.

SPECIMEN SKINS OF KING CHEETAH TAKEN TO DATE

	Year	Location	Specimen	Collector	Current Owner
1	1926	Macheke Rhodesia	flat skin (holotype)	Mr. D. Fraser	Destroyed *circa* 1950/151; National Museum & Monuments of Rhodesia
2	1925	Bikita Rhodesia	mounted skin	Mr. H. N. Watters	British Museum (Natural History)
3	1925	Bikita Rhodesia	mounted skin	Mr. H. N. Watters	Natal Museum South Africa
4	1925	Melsetter Rhodesia	flat skin	Mutambara Mission	Unknown
5	1926	Seki Rhodesia	flat skin	Mr. Lacey	Unknown
6	1927	Mt. Selinda Rhodesia	flat skin	Maj. A. L. Cooper	British Museum (Natural History)
7	1928	Bikita Rhodesia	mounted skin	Mr. H. N. Watters	South African Museum, Cape Town
8	1935	Birchenough Bridge Rhodesia	flat skin	Mr. D. Townley	Sir Archibald James
9	1940	Messina S. Africa	skin/skull	Mr. S. van der Walt	Mr. J. Joubert
10	1942	Tjolotjo Rhodesia	flat skin	Mr. N. L. Dacomb	Kaffrarian Museum King Williams Town South Africa
11	1956	Inyanga Rhodesia	flat skin	Mr. Waddington	Mr. Meriden
12	1960	Tuli Botswana	flat skin	Mr. L. Van Niekerk	Mr. L. Van Niekerk
13	1960s	Rakops Botswana	flat skin	Mr. C. Freeman	Mr. C. Freeman
14	1960s	Rakops Botswana	flat skin	Mr. C. Freeman	stolen (whereabouts unknown)
15	1960s	Rakops Botswana	flat skin	Mr. C. Freeman	stolen ,,
16	1960s	Rakops Botswana	flat skin	Mr. C. Freeman	stolen ,,
17	1960	Botswana/ Transvaal?	flat skin	Mr. R. B. Ivy	Ivy's Curio Shop South Africa
18	1965	Botswana/ Transvaal?	flat skin	Mr. R. B. Ivy	Ivy's Curio Shop South Africa
19	1966	Botswana/ Transvaal?	flat skin	Mr. R. B. Ivy	Ivy's Curio Shop South Africa
20	1968	Tuli Botswana	flat skin	Red Shields	Unknown
21	1971	Moijabana Botswana	flat skin	Dr. R. H. N. Smithers	National Museum of Botswana
22	1974	Mozambique	flat skin	Mr. L. Von Tonder	Mr. L. Von Tonder

CONFIRMED LIVE KING CHEETAH SPECIMENS

		Year	Location
1		1974-1979	Kruger National Park
2	captive born cub	1981	Seaview Game Park (now at De Wildt.)
3)	captive born cubs	1981-1987	De Wildt Breeding Centre
4)			De Wildt ,,
5)			De Wildt ,,
6)			De Wildt ,,
7)			De Wildt ,,
8)			De Wildt ,,
9)			De Wildt ,,
10)			De Wildt ,,
11)			De Wildt ,,
12)			De Wildt ,,
13)			De Wildt ,,
14)			De Wildt ,,
15		1986	Kruger National Park
16		1986	Kruger National Park

Bibliography

*** 1979. Vonds G'n In Bosse, Maar Tuis. *Beeld*, Johannesburg, January 27, p. 5.

*** 1979. Cheetah with a Difference. *Custos*, Vol. 8, No. 8, pp. 42-43. Pretoria: National Parks Board of South Africa.

*** 1987. Geparde-Schutz durch Streifen. *GEO*, March, No. 3, pp. 179-82.

*** 1936. A Leopard Which "Changed Its Spots"!—A Specimen From Somaliland With Markings Resembling a Chita. *The Illustrated London News*, Vol. 188, June 6, p. 1012.

*** 1966. Rare King Cheetah Skin Not For Sale. *The Star*, Johannesburg, December 6.

*** 1987. "... but the cheetah's future is rosier". *New Scientist*, Vol. 114, No. 1555, p. 27.

*** 1982. "The king cheetah puzzle". *Wildlife* (BBC), Vol. 24, No. 2, p. 73.

Aarde, R. J. van & Ann van Dyk, 1986. Inheritance of the king coat colour pattern in cheetahs *Acinoyx jubatus*. *Journal of Zoology*, London, Series A, Vol. 209, pp. 573-78.

Ansell, W. F. H., 1967. An Aberrant Leopard From Rhodesia. *Arnoldia* (*Rhodesia*), Vol. 3, No. 3, pp. 1-6, 4 plates.

Bottriell, Lena G. 1979. Mystery of the king cheetah remains. *The Star*, Johannesburg, June 13.

Bottriell, Lena G., & Paul Bottriell, 1980. Su Alteza o Chita Real. *Diário de Noticias*, Lisbon, September 21, pp. 27-28.

Bottriell, Lena Godsall, 1987. The King Of The Cats? *EXCELLENCE*, Sun International, Vol. 3, No. 1, pp. 52-56.

Brand, D. J., 1980. Breeding endangered species in captivity (Third world conference). *International Zoo Yearbook*, Vol. 20, pp. 107-12.

Brand, D. J., 1981. A King Cheetah born at the Cheetah Breeding and Research Centre, Natl. Zool. Gdns. of South Africa, Pretoria. *Proceedings 36th. Annual Conference of International Union of Zool. Gdns.* meeting in Washington D.C., September 27–October 3, p. 111.

Brand, D. J., 1982. Personal communication: letter to Lena G. Bottriell, February 11.

Buckmaster, John, 1928. Personal communication: letter to Major A. L. Cooper, July 14.

Cabrera, Angel L., 1932. (Género *Acinonyx* Brookes, in:) Los Mamíferos De Marruecos. *Trabajos Museo Nacional de Ciencias Naturales. Madrid.* — Serie Zoológica, No. 57, p. 190-91.

Chapmen, Abel, 1928. The Rhodesian Cheetah. *Field*, London, Vol. 151, April 19, p. 654.

Cooper, A. L., 1926. A Curious Skin. *Field*, London, Vol. 148, No. 3851, October 14, p. 690.

Cooper, A. L., 1927. Notes on *Acinonyx rex* (Cooper's Cheetah). *South African Journal of Science*, Vol. 24, December, pp. 343-45.

Cubitt, Gerald, 1986. *Portraits of the African Wild* (pp. 186-88). London: Admiral Books.

Dacomb, Neal, 1974. Personal communication: letter to Mr. Noel Robertson, February 16.

Dollman, Guy, 1929. The King Cheetah. *Natural History Magazine*, London, Vol. 2, No. 9, pp. 1-6.

Dower, Kenneth C. Gandar, 1935. In Quest of the Spotted Lion. The Needle in the Aberdare Haystack. *Field*, London, Vol. 166, July 6, p. 21.

Doyle, Arthur Conan, 1929. Strange Animals. *Our African Winter*. London: John Murray.

Eaton, Randal, 1974. *The Cheetah: The Biology, Ecology and Behavior of an Endangered Species*. New York: Van Nostrand Reinhold Co.

Goosen, Helena, 1986. Striking coat for a king. *South African Panorama*, Vol. 31, No. 5, pp. 48-50. Pretoria: Bureau for Information.

Graaf, G. de, 1974. A Familiar Pattern Deviation of the Cheetah (*Acinonyx jubatus*). *Custos*, Vol. 3, No. 12, pp. 2, 28. Pretoria: National Parks Board of South Africa.

Greaves, William, 1978. Chasing the most elusive legend on four legs. *Daily Mail*, London, September 4, p. 7.

Guggisberg, C. A. W., 1975. *Wild Cats of the World*. London: David & Charles.

Gunther, Albert, 1885. Note on a supposed Melanotic Variety of the Leopard, from South Africa. *Proceedings of the Zoological Society of London* (for 1885), March 3, pp. 243-45.

Gunther, Albert, 1886. Second Note on the Melanotic Variety of the South-African Leopard. *Proceedings of the Zoological Society of London* (for 1886), April 6, pp. 203-205.

Harper, Francis, 1945. *Extinct and Vanishing Mammals of the Old World*. Special Publication No. 12, pp. 286-88. New York: American Committee for International Wild Life Protection.

Heran, Ivan, 1976. *Animal Coloration: The nature and purpose of colours in vertebrates*. London: Hamlyn.

Heuvelmans, Bernard, 1958. *On the Track of Unknown Animals*. London: Rupert Hart-Davis.

Hichens, William, 1928. Africa's Mystery Beasts. *Wide World*, London, Vol. 62, December, pp. 171-176.

Hichens, William, 1937. African Mystery Beasts. *Discovery*, London, Vol. 28, December, pp. 369-71.

Hills, Daphne M., & Reay H. N. Smithers, 1980. The "King Cheetah": A historical review. *Arnoldia (Zimbabwe)*, Vol. 9, No. 1, pp. 1-23.

Jackson, Peter, 1986. Personal communication: letter to Simon Stuart, October 7.

Jamer, Archibald Sir, 1962. The Puzzle of King Cheetahs. *Field*, London, Vol. 219, No. 5706, May 24, pp. 1018-19.

Keogh, Hilary, 1979. *Acinonyx rex* Pocock, 1927. Personal communication, March 1.

Kock, Leon de, 1979. Is hy die laaste in die wereld? Soektog na unieke dier. *Beeld*, Johannesburg, July 26, pp. 1-2.

Kretzoi, Miklos, 1929. Taxonomiai megjegyzések. *Paracinonyx n. gen.* (Generotypus: *Acinonyx rex* Pocock, 1927). *Felida Tanulmányok*, Budapest (2. Aeluroidea Kozlemeny), pp. 10-11.

Labuschagne, Willie, 1987. Personal communication: letter to Lena G. Bottriell, May 5.

Lydekker, Richard, 1893-94. *The Royal Natural History*. 6 vols. (Mammals Vol. 1, pp. 442-46). London: Frederick Warne & Co.

Lydekker, Richard, 1895. (The Hunting Leopard, in:)—*A Handbook to the Carnivora Pt. 1., Cats, Civets & Mongooses*, pp. 202-203. London: J. F. Shaw.

Maberley, C. T. Astley, 1959. *The animals of Rhodesia*, pp. 120-21. Cape Town: Howard Timmins.

McBride, Chris, 1977. *The White Lions of Timbavati*, p. 96. London & New York: Paddington Press.

Meester, J., 1962. King Cheetah in Northern Transvaal. *African Wild Life*, Vol. 16, No. 1, pp. 81-82.

Mivart, St. George Jackson, 1881. (The Woolly Cheetah (*Felis lanea*) in:) *The Cat*, pp. 429-30. London: John Murray.

Norman, Charles, 1979. King Of The Cheetahs: In Search of a Legendary Animal. *Scope*, Durban, Vol. 14, No. 17, pp. 88-93.

Oakes, Philip, 1987. Spot the difference. *YOU Magazine*, London, May 10-16, pp. 36-37.

O'Brien, Stephen J., & David E. Wildt, et al., 1983. The Cheetah is Depauperate in Genetic Variation. *Science*, Washington, Vol. 221, No. 4609, pp. 459-62.

O'Brien, Stephen J., David E. Wildt & Mitchell Bush, 1986. The Cheetah in Genetic Peril. *Scientific American*, New York, Vol. 254, No. 5, pp. 68-76.

O'Brien, Stephen J., et al., 1987. East African cheetahs: Evidence for two population bottlenecks? *Proceedings of the National Academy of Sciences*, Washington D.C., Vol. 84, No. 2, pp. 508-11.

Penrith, Michael J., 1987. Personal communication: letter to Paul & Lena Bottriell, January 16.

Pocock, Reginald Innes, 1921. An Interesting Cheetah. *Field*, London, Vol. 137, No. 3560, March 19, p. 352.

Pocock, Reginald Innes, 1926. Variation of the Pattern in Leopards. *Field*, London, Vol. 148, No. 3852, October 21, p. 707.

Pocock, Reginald Innes, 1927a. Description of a New Species of Cheetah (*Acinonyx*). *Proceedings of the Zoological Society of London*, Pt. 1, pp. 245-51, 257.

Pocock, Reginald Innes, 1927b. The New Cheetah from Rhodesia. *Journal of the Society for the Preservation of the Fauna of the Empire*, New Series, Pt. 7, pp. 17-19. London: H. F. & G. Witherby.

Pocock, Reginald Innes, 1927c. The New Cheetah. *Field*, London, Vol. 149, No. 3877, April 14, p. 635.

Pocock, Reginald Innes, 1927d. *Annals and Magazine of Natural History*, London, Series 9, Vol. 20, p. 212.

Pocock, Reginald Innes, 1928. The Rhodesian Cheetah. *Field*, London, Vol. 151, No. 3928, April 5, p. 593.

Pocock, Reginald Innes, 1932. The leopards of Africa. *Proceedings of the Zoological Society of London*, Vol. 1, pp. 550-51.

Pocock, Reginald Innes, 1935. Exhibitions and Notices. *Proceedings of the Zoological Society of London*, Vol. 2, pp. 733-735.

Pocock, Reginald Innes, 1939. *The fauna of British India including Ceylon and Burma.* Mammalia Vol. 1, Primates & Carnivora (Sec. edition), p. 325, footnote. London: Taylor and Francis Ltd.

Roberts, Austin, 1951. *The Mammals of South Africa* (pp. 182-83, 564). Johannesburg: Trustees of the ''The Mammals of South Africa'' Book Fund.

Robinson, Roy, 1976. Homologous Genetic Variation in the Felidae. *Genetica*, Vol. 46, pp. 1-31.

Schenck, Leoné, 1979. In Search of the King of the Cheetahs. *Family Radio & TV*, Johannesburg, September 10-16, pp. 42-44.

Sclater, Philip Lutley, 1877. *Felis lanea* (Description of the woolly cheetah). *Proceedings of the Zoological Society of London* (for 1877), June 19, pp. 532-34.

Sclater, Philip Lutley, 1878. Mr. P. L. Sclater on *Felis lanea*. *Proceedings of the Zoological Society of London* (for 1878), June 18, pp. 655-56.

Sclater, Philip Lutley, 1884. The woolly cheetah. *Proceedings of the Zoological Society of London* (for 1884), November 4, p. 476.

Sclater, William Lutley, 1900. *Fauna of South Africa. The Mammals.* 2 vols. (Vol. 1, pp. 36-37). London: R. H. Porter.

Shortridge, Guy C., 1934. *The mammals of South West Africa.* 2 vols. (Vol. 1, pp. 104-110). London: Heinemann.

Smithers, Reay H. N., 1971. *The mammals of Botswana.* Salisbury (Harare): Trustees of the National Museums and Monuments of Rhodesia.

Smithers, Reay H. N., 1978. The Serval *Felis serval* Schreber, 1776. *South African Journal of Wildlife Research*, Vol. 8, pp. 29-37.

Smithers, Reay H. N., 1983. *The Mammals Of The Southern African Subregion.* University of Pretoria.

Stevenson-Hamilton, James, 1941. *Our South African National Parks.* Cape Town: Cape Times Limited.

Stevenson-Hamilton, James, 1947. *Wild Life in South Africa.* London: Cassell.

Toit, J. T. du, 1986. Personal communication: letter to Paul Bottriell, June 7.

Varaday, Desmond, 1964. *Gara Yaka, The Story of a Cheetah.* New York: E. P. Dutton & Co.

240

Ward, Rowland, 1935. *Records of big game*. 10th edition (pp. 385-86). London: Rowland Ward Publications.

Ward, Rowland, 1980. *Game Animals of Africa*. Portfolio 1. Johannesburg: Rowland Ward's (Southern Africa).

Welfare, Simon, & John Fairley, 1982. Nunda. *Arthur C. Clarke's Mysterious World* (pp. 199-202). London: Fontana/Collins.

Wildt, David E. et al., 1983. Seminal Quality in the Cheetah and Domestic Cat. *Biology of Reproduction*, Vol. 29, pp. 1019-25.

Wright, Michael, & Sally Walters, 1980. *The Book of the Cat*. London: Pan Books.

Wrogemann, Nan, 1975. *Cheetah Under the Sun*. New York: McGraw-Hill.

International Society of Cryptozoology

Readers wanting to learn more about controversial animals are invited to join the International Society of Cryptozoology (ISC). This organisation serves as a focal point for the investigation, analysis, publication, and discussion of all matters relating to animals of unexpected form or size, or unexpected occurrence in time or space. It encourages scientific examination of all relevant evidence and is recognised as the most authoritative organisation devoted to cryptozoology. ISC recognises that cryptozoology engenders sometimes emotional debates, about such phenomena as Nessie, the Abominable Snowman and Sasquatch, and endeavours to address such issues objectively by following established scientific methods. Through its quarterly newsletter and its scholarly journal *Cryptozoology*, issued once a year, it disseminates cryptozoological information, including records of sightings as well as analyses of evidence provided by photographs, sonar tracks, footprint casts, tissue samples, hair samples etc.
ISC is governed by a Board of Directors which includes several senior scientists, which meets regularly, and which organises meetings at venues in the United States, Europe and elsewhere. Membership is open to all interested persons.

For details about membership write to:

P.O. Box 43070, Tucson, Arizona 85733, U.S.A.